Patient Power

PATIENT POWER

Overcoming Chronic Illness

James Marshall Galbraith

BENCHMARK BOOKS • SAN MARINO, CALIFORNIA

Library of Congress Catalog Card Number 95-76505

International Standard Book Number: 0-942246-02-0

Manufactured in the United States of America.

*Everything can be taken from a man but one thing:
the last of human freedoms—to choose one's attitude
in any given set of circumstances.*
                              Dr. Victor E. Frankl
                              Man's Search for Meaning

*If you have a chronic disease, you need not be emo-
tionally handicapped if you can continually strive to
be able-hearted.*
                              JoAnn LeMaistre, Ph.D.
                              Beyond Rage

My profound thanks to my wife Peggy for her love and inspiration, and to my good friend and tennis partner Chris Madison, whose printing company ColorGraphics did such a splendid job of book production.

Table of Contents

INTRODUCTION

In 1977, I was thirty-five years old and the picture of health. Other than the usual childhood and sports injuries and a tonsillectomy, my only experience with the medical profession had been vicarious. That year, both my law partner and my sister-in-law died after lengthy and brave battles with dreaded diseases, melanoma (a form of cancer) and lupus erythematosus. They were to become models for me in my fight against a chronic, degenerative, and hereditary disease.

I would have been shocked to learn at that point in my life that as many as one in five Americans suffered from chronic illness, or permanent disabilities, and that most people had family, friends, or associates with some form of incurable or irreparable condition. Some conditions, such as untreatable allergies, may not seem too serious, but they place exasperating restrictions on patients' daily lives. And, while the symptoms may come and go, they do not go away.

When you are young, you believe you are invincible and that physical problems you have heard about in others will never happen to you. Mercifully, you do not ever consider the eventual reality that virtually all of us will deal with the chronic physical condition of old age. My youthful ignorance was to be abruptly rectified.

Patients do not generally recognize what an important role they have to play in their own medical care. The historical relationship between patient and physician has been a passive one, with the patient trusting that all is in good hands. We have always put physicians on pedestals, assuming they were somehow God-like in knowing what ails the patient and what treatment and medication to prescribe. In reality, any chronic patient soon learns that the only thing more amazing than what doctors know is what they don't. And what they especially don't know is you. You have a lifetime of accumulated information, some of which can prove indispensable to your proper care. It is a blessing to find a physician who can elicit that important information from you. It does not emerge from one long informational appointment. It surfaces as the illness evolves and as the doctor-patient relationship strengthens. It is the result of a lot of trial and error, false hopes, medical advances, and attitude adjustments. These adjustments involve your family, friends, and associates, as changes in your physical reality impact the nature of all these relationships.

My experience with the lingering and devastating illnesses of my law partner and the older sister of my wife,

Peggy, would change my perception of the doctor-patient relationship. My partner originally saw an internist in 1970 about an ugly-looking mole on his leg. He was told to keep an eye on it and to make an appointment with a specialist if it changed. Months later, he saw a cancer specialist and had a series of biopsies taken, only to find that he had a malignant melanoma, a highly malignant tumor of the skin, which often spreads so rapidly that it is fatal within months of its recognition. Worse, the tumor had metastasized (i.e., spread). He was told there were some experimental treatments that could prove helpful, but that his chances of survival were extremely slim. Had my partner been able to provide a case history of frequent and severe sunburn, prior to the general acceptance of sunscreens, which might have alerted doctors earlier to the possibility of melanoma, he might well have had preventive surgery in time.

My sister-in-law's condition was also exacerbated by exposure to ultra-violet rays. The onset of her symptoms may have been hastened by countless hours on the tennis court in her youth. Lupus is an auto-immune disease—the villain is an overly aggressive immune system. It can attack any organ of the body, but its most frequent target is the kidney. It also attacks the lining of the joints, causing arthritis. When she first developed the arthritic symptoms and rashes common to lupus, in the early 1960's, the control of this condition was not well understood. She was treated with occasionally high dosages of a steroid known as prednisone, with many troublesome side effects I would later learn about myself. If her case history had been developed sooner, and she had been referred earlier on to a rheumatologist specializing in lupus, it is possible that the disease might not have proved fatal. It is rarely fatal today.

With the onset of my own symptoms in 1977 to 1979, I was ineffectual in helping my internist discover the nature of my illness. While I would eventually know how important it was to be pro-active with my physician to assist in early detection and treatment, I was initially in a stage of denial. I steadfastly refused to accept that I was ill. I assumed I was just under a lot of stress and therefore vulnerable to flu-type symptoms. I did not really consider the possibility that I was confronted with the onset of a chronic and degenerative illness until that conclusion was practically inescapable.

By 1980, my medical symptoms were to force my retirement from the fourteen hour per day practice of law in the field of corporate finance. Instead, I would be "of counsel" to my former partners and clients and would attempt to adopt the business of many of my clients, turning troubled companies around. I was fortunate to have a close friend and client with whom to launch such a career. Looking back, I have no idea why I thought the entrepreneurial world was going to be more under my control than the practice of law. As it turned out, the 1980's proved to be a wild ride, with plenty of distraction from focusing on my worsening symptoms.

Those years were filled with excitement and challenge and are chronicled in two of my previous books, *The Money Tree*, and *Fear of Failure*, but at the time I repressed the urge to discuss what a profound effect my declining health had on those years (and probably *vice versa*). Perhaps I felt it would detract from my primary messages that the American Dream is still alive and well and that the "fear of failure" should be used as an empowering, rather than paralyzing, force. Or, perhaps, it just seemed too personal. Now, though, as we approach a new century in which health is going to be a central focus of an aging population, it seems important for people to know that they can singlehandedly make a difference in their own medical care.

On reflection, I could not have written this book a few years ago. I had not yet come to grips with my own struggle to overcome chronic illness. I had put the fear of the disease behind me and no longer seethed with anger at my predicament. But I had not made the creative adjustments in my life patterns and priorities that would be necessary to transcend my symptoms and lead a meaningful existence. I had yet to strike a balance with my physician between the risks and rewards of a seductive but treacherous treatment of my symptoms. My family and friends would help me deal with my disappointment at the absence of a "miracle" cure and would help empower me to choose life's possibilities over the confines of victimhood.

I

BECOMING A PATIENT

Bleeding internally can be unnerving, even terrifying. I first experienced it at the age of thirty-five. It signalled the beginning of an unexpected and confounding journey as a patient in America. It was a pilgrimage for which I was ill-prepared.

For my intestinal bleeding, I was referred by my internist to a proctologist. He conducted a sigmoidoscopy of the colon, enabling him to get photographs and biopsies of the affected tissue. The doctor said little following the examination, prompting me to ask what the possible causes of bleeding might be. He explained that the most common causes were hemorrhoids and ulcerations, but that all he really observed was inflammation. I pressed for

1

other possibilities. "It's possible it could be a malignancy," he said. "We'll have to wait for the lab results." And, with that, he was gone.

Days later, I spoke to the proctologist. He told me that the good news was that all the biopsies were negative (which really was positive—medicalese and legalese are alike in that they create confusion and anxiety in the layman). The bad news, he added, was that he was not sure what had caused the bleeding. If it recurred, I was to call his office immediately and make an appointment.

I was both relieved and upset. Of course, I was glad there was no malignancy, but I had a bleeding problem, for some unknown reason, and nothing was being done about it!

Weeks later, more bleeding and more tests were to leave me just as ignorant of the nature of my problem. My reaction this time was to pretend it never happened. Since ignorance is bliss, I was happy to have my health for many months thereafter. Surely if there were anything seriously wrong, a specialist would know. It would take additional warning signals for me to start listening to my body and taking seriously my responsibilities as a patient.

Peggy was already sensing that something was seriously wrong with me. Being out in the sun became very oppressive to me. My energy and endurance seemed to melt as the temperature rose. The logistics of simple tasks became more difficult. I did not have my former strength, coordination, or balance. Most of all, I had no staying power. Peggy remembers my trying to set up for a backyard dinner party and literally being unable to do it. A year earlier, I would have handled it enthusiastically and effortlessly. She also reminded me of a ski trip to Colorado when the power went out on the lifts. I had to carry one of the children up a steep slope to a restaurant, where we were meeting another family for lunch. Of course, it was exhausting, but I did not bounce back from it. I could barely ski down the mountain after lunch and had great difficulty helping the children get their skis, boots, and poles to the car. I had never felt so utterly exhausted and helpless. That evening I was in a fog, not myself, and not understanding why.

A brief encounter with what I thought was an appendicitis attack on vacation was to provide an eventual clue to my condition. Fortunately for me, my family and I were barbequeing on the beach with a former NFL lineman when I was hit with acute abdominal pain. Our friend had no problem carrying me to the car and racing me to Scripps Memorial Hospital in La Jolla, California. After a thorough examination, they pronounced that the pain was due to violent spasming in the colon, which along with the intestinal bleeding was to assist in my eventual diagnosis the following year.

I switched my care soon thereafter to an internist with gastroenterological training, who prescribed medication to control my occasional intestinal spasming. But I hadn't seen anything yet. In 1979, Peggy and I went on a weekend with friends to Puerta Vallarta, the last vacation I was to have without the difficulties of my as yet undiagnosed health problem.

We were very careful about what we ate and drank south of the border, but evidently not careful enough. By the time we returned home, I was extremely sick with flu-like symptoms. For weeks and to a lesser extent for months, I experienced chronic diarrhea, abdominal pain, fever, bloating, nausea, and general shakiness. My weight plummeted more than twenty-five pounds to about 170. The doctors looked at the possibilities of amoebic dysentery or a parasite, but ruled them out over a period of weeks.

Looking back, I clearly contributed to the slow pace

of this progress. I was a difficult patient. While it is a common response to the onset of chronic illness to deny it, I took this to an extreme. At first, I simply would not allow the symptoms, the diagnosis, or the logistics of appointments and lab tests, to interfere with my work or my life. As the reality became more clear, I realized that I was no longer in charge of my life and was very reactive and upset. I was not asking "Why me?" but was exclaiming "I don't have time for this!"

Eventually, it sank in that I had a serious problem and had better start prioritizing its solution. Only then did my gastroenterological internist start piecing together a comprehensive case history. Following up on my previous intestinal symptoms, he began to consider that I might have a chronic inflammatory disease. I had the usual G.I. (gastro-intestinal) tests, the upper G.I., using barium to see the small intestine by X-ray, the lower G.I., using a barium enema to see the large intestine, and the first of many colonoscopies. This latter procedure proved to have its lighter moments. The patient is supposed to be fairly heavily sedated while the doctor maneuvers a flexible scope through about 60 centimeters of meanderings of the intestine, about 36 centimeters farther than my earlier sigmoidoscopy. My internist soon found that the usual 50-milligram dosage of Demerol did not sufficiently sedate me. At one point, as the scope bumped gently into the wall of the intestine, I was intently watching on the monitor and asked if we were stuck. After some additional medication, I was still asking unfocused questions about the procedure, which was evidently an unwanted distraction. Afterwards, the doctor said, "Next time, we're giving you 100 milligrams!"

Close examination of photographs and biopsies performed through the scope revealed ulcerations in the large intestine known as apthous ulcers. They were the earliest lesions of a condition known as Crohn's disease, which I would later learn is a form of inflammatory bowel disease and is also known as regional enteritis. My doctor theorized that the onset of symptoms had been triggered by a bacterial or viral agent picked up in Mexico. He explained that an unusual vulnerability to the condition was thought to be hereditary. I had no idea what it was to mean to have Crohn's, but had a sense of relief knowing that "they" (the medical profession) at least knew what I had. I was exhausted. It had been four excruciating and anxiety-ridden months between my acute symptoms and my initial diagnosis.

This was an extraordinarily stressful time for me. The loss of my law partner had left a gaping hole in both my personal and professional lives. The anguish of dealing with his dying and his death was excruciating. Not only had I lost a good friend, my partners and I were all going to have to work longer and harder. Because he and I had been the only corporate partners, I was initially bearing the primary burden.

The subsequent passing of Peggy's sister left us stunned over the loss of a wonderful person and the inexplicability of death out of order. The passing of two people so dear, still in their thirties, was my first close confrontation with death and with my own mortality. I was confounded by the why of it. I was sorry I had not known them even better. I wondered if I could have done more to ease their suffering. I hoped I would be able to be helpful to their families, out of respect. But I was also confronted with the fear of death, and of dying. It was uncertain, unsettling, and unpleasant.

Perhaps this stressful time helped trigger the onset of my own symptoms, perhaps not. There is still much that is not known about this and many other medical conditions.

I had been in close touch with my mother, who had suffered for years with severe intestinal problems, which she referred to as inflammatory bowel disease. When I told her I had been diagnosed with Crohn's disease, she said, "My dear, that's what I've had for years!"

Feeling foolish, I responded, "But you never called it that."

I knew from my mother's experience that there was no known cure for this condition and that the control of symptoms sometimes required the use of steroids, such as prednisone or Decadron, which had very harmful side effects. The inflammation of the intestine, and in rare cases the esophagus, was caused by the body's own immune system, which identified normal tissue as foreign and attacked it unmercifully. Steroids would inhibit the immune system in order to block or at least restrain the attacks. If steroids were overused, though, it could block the immune system from performing its critical functions to the body and could result in numerous other unwanted side-effects.

My symptoms, which I heard referred to as "the 24-hour flu for life," did not subside. My doctor tried numerous medications to alleviate the symptoms and experimented with my diet and regimen. I learned from experience that a low-fiber diet could reduce pain, temporarily, but would increase nausea. I also learned that I could stand pain more than I could tolerate nausea.

One of the most helpful sources of information about Crohn's disease in the 1980's was the *Crohn's-Colitis Update*, published by the Blinder Research Foundation for Crohn's Disease. Meyer Blinder is best known for heading up the controversial investment banking firm Blinder, Robinson & Co. out of Denver, Colorado.

Both Blinder's wife and son suffer from Crohn's. His wife endured six intestinal surgeries before her condition was finally diagnosed. This so upset Blinder that he pledged $1 million to a new foundation dedicated to find a cure.

Blinder's son had the onset of symptoms at college at the age of twenty. He had suffered waves of gut-wrenching spasms, diarrhea, and bouts of "flu." His reaction to his Crohn's diagnosis says a lot about the disease's perception. He told his parents, "Don't tell anyone!" For a time, they honored a vow of silence not even to tell his younger brother and sister. The young Crohn's victim was quoted by the Denver *Post* as saying:

> At one time or another, everyone's had stomach trouble or flu. It's not hard to feel what it would be like if the cramps and diarrhea never went away and hurt a hundred times more. Bowel disease is too close to personal experience, too dirty, too humiliating, too scary. You don't want it to happen to you, but you can't avoid thinking about it. So you edge away. You detach. And that's when your silence talks.

I was disappointed when, in 1990, the Blinder Foundation ceased publication of the informative and useful *Crohn's-Colitis Update* because of its high production cost. They reasoned that the funds would be better used in hard scientific research.

I actively sought additional input and ideas about my condition. I received an article stating that a Crohn's patient could spend up to $500,000 in lifetime medical bills, but that the condition would not kill him (although he would sometimes wish it would). The article went on to say that the Crohn's patient would feel like half his life was spent in the bathroom and the other half looking for one! Later, I was saddened to read in the paper that a friend of my parents with a terrible case of Crohn's had shot himself, rather than further endure the disease's misery and indignities. That was all pretty powerful input.

But somehow my mother seemed to stagger along despite this miserable condition. She provided my most valuable inspiration to learn to co-exist with a disease that at best was unpleasant and debilitating and could be far worse. I recall reading in *The Merck Manual*, for physicians, that death from Crohn's could occur due to obstruction, hemorrhage, perforation, or inanition (starvation, due to malabsorption). I would have a number of scares over the years. In 1982, I began having excruciating combinations of pain, nausea, vomiting, and increasing abdominal pressure. My internist suspected an obstruction and rushed me to the hospital for another colonoscopy and possible surgery. What followed were some troubling, yet comical experiences.

Before my procedure, I returned some official calls from my hospital room. One of them was from my literary agent with the exciting news that he had a potential paperback publisher for *The Money Tree*, my book about how to succeed in the free enterprise system. But he cautioned, "you'll have to do about twenty-one cities in nineteen days." I explained that I could not have met that schedule even without the possible obstruction surgery. He pushed, knowing that it might be our only chance at a soft-cover deal. "Don't you realize this is how it's done?" I truly did understand, but it was a lost opportunity.

The time came to prepare me to go down to a surgical room. I was completely reamed out of all solid matter and was first to be sedated through an I.V. A nurse entered the room and started setting up. Then, as she inserted the I.V. needle, she accidentally pushed it back through the vein and blood began to spurt. She was completely paralyzed by what had happened. I asked her to call the doctor, but she did not seem to understand me. Meanwhile, I held my pillow over my arm to try to stop the bleeding. At this very moment, a man entered the room announcing he was with the hospital's quality assurance program. Then, he saw the blood and said, "Oh my God! Let's get those sheets changed!" I told him that wasn't my highest priority at the moment, but order was soon restored.

At long last, the sedative was flowing into my bloodstream when a nurse entered the room, clipboard in hand. "You're Mr. Galbraith?"

"That's right."

"And you're here for the colostomy?" (A colostomy involves the complete removal of the colon and its replacement with a bag outside the body.)

"No!" I protested, "A colonoscopy!"

"Don't worry," she reassured. "They'll get it right."

"I'm worried," I said, as I faded out of consciousness.

The colonoscopy happily showed the apparent intestinal blockage to be purely muscular and not requiring surgery. As I came to from heavy sedation, I had a panic attack, fearing they might have done the colostomy after all. But I was quickly satisfied that I was still a whole person.

Since then, I have altered my view of a colostomy. If my condition could be cured merely by enduring the indignity of a waste-collecting pouch, I would do it in an instant. Unfortunately, this procedure only works for ulcerative colitis.

With increasing frequency, I began to experience the symptoms of inflammation and apthous ulcers throughout the esophagus as well as the intestine. The throat ulcerations made it extremely difficult to talk, swallow, breathe, and sleep. Drugs such as Vicodin, a powerful pain-killer, were virtually useless to lessen the pain. These "sieges," as I called them, would last a few weeks or longer and would immobilize me much of the day. The only bright side of this was that it might make me medically "interesting."

Because I no longer worked in downtown Los Angeles near my gastroenterological internist and his hospital, I decided I should pick a local Pasadena internist with ready access to our nearby hospital. I found an internist who counted many of my friends among his patients, and found him very thorough and very comfortable. I would look to him to keep me extremely healthy, except for my underlying condition. My only reservation after seeing him for several years is that he is nearly twenty years older than I, but he has gone out of his way to assure me that he signed a ten-year lease!

For my gastroenterological needs, I was fortunate to be referred to Dr. Gary Gitnick, a respected authority in the field at UCLA (where he became Chief-of-Staff). Interestingly, he was also the editor of the *Crohn's-Colitis Update*. My first impression of Gary was that he was smart, professional, and slightly distant. Over the past fifteen years, we have become friends and I have learned what an extraordinary person he is. Despite his busy lecture schedule around the country and beyond, and his duties heading up the hospital, he has always been accessible to me when I was in need. He is also actively involved in the community. Through the Fulfillment Fund, he helps to send deserving inner-city students to college.

Because my symptoms intensified each day, I found in about 1981 or 1982 that I was most productive working at home in the afternoons. There I could work in a sort of "zone," unaffected by meetings and office interaction. I came to realize that, as the day wore on, I had to run on adrenaline to have effective people time. This proved exhausting.

I think that far less than half my productive output has been done at the office the past fifteen years. Peggy always knew this, but it wasn't always clear to my doctors. Before we knew Gary Gitnick very well, he was asking generally how I was doing. "And you're working half-days?"

Peggy laughed. "Actually, if he's awake, he's working."

"That's not true," I protested.

"It's true," she concluded firmly.

Mistakes happen in the best hospitals and the most professional doctors' offices. I experienced my share of them. One in particular stands out. I was having my annual physical at my internist's office late on a Friday afternoon, a difficult time of day for me. The technician seemed perturbed by the computer readout of my EKG and reran it. My internist came in and told me that the computer-generated results indicated that I had had a mild heart attack.

I spent the weekend worrying about this and called Gary Gitnick. He asked me to fax him the test results, which I did. Within hours, he called back and told me he had the results run on a computer and that the electrical lead on the left side of my chest had been mispositioned. If it were placed properly, it would read "normal." I was back in the doctor's office in no time and the re-run test was in fact normal.

I was also impacted by computer analyses of my blood tests, which started consistently flagging the possibility of an auto-immune disease such as lupus, which had afflicted my sister-in-law but is rare in men. A more specific test ruled out lupus in my case, but there were evidently some common denominators in auto-immune diseases.

I had hopes that my case would be interesting to Dr. Gitnick, given his distinguished reputation and his commitment to Crohn's research. It turned out I was only the third out of his hundreds of patients to have auto-immune symptoms in the intestine and the esophagus. Since Dr. Crohn got to name a disease by distinguishing it from ulcerative colitis, I kidded Gary Gitnick that his three patients with severe esophageal symptoms and less severe, though chronic intestinal symptoms, should be re-diagnosed with "Gitnick's disease."

While it was exciting to be seeing someone who might contribute to a Crohn's cure or improved treatment of symptoms, nothing too revolutionary came along, despite some high hopes for such drugs as 5-ASA (known as 5-Aminosalicylic acid), an anti-inflammatory, and 6MP (mercaptopurine), an immunosuppressant. Research into the causes of auto-immune diseases, such as Crohn's, lupus, rheumatoid arthritis, and multiple sclerosis was expected to be enhanced by AIDS research. While the problem with an auto-immune condition is one of an overly-aggressive, rather than deficient, immune system, an understanding of the immune system and the immune response is required in both instances. But, so far, it appears they are not near a research breakthrough.

Gary Gitnick proved to be a conservative practitioner, often resisting my pleas for a more aggressive treatment to bring my miserable symptoms under control. Instead, we tried medication designed to treat individual symptoms as they arose, spasming, diarrhea, nausea, inflammation, and pain. I believe, subconsciously, Gary may have been waiting for more serious intestinal symptoms to develop, an obstruction, a fistula (an abnormal passage from an absess through the intestinal wall), or a perforation of the intestine. These are all common complications that follow the normal progression of the disease in the intestine.

If my intestinal symptoms had progressed, I believe Gary would have been more comfortable prescribing steroids to reduce the damage from my own immune system. But he continued to emphasize the immediate side-effects and the long-term negatives of steroid use. The immediate effects can be stomach or duodenal ulcers, insomia, weight gain, hypertension, and emotional disturbances. Longer use can cause thinning of the skin, a slowing of the healing process, brittle bones, depression, and seizures. Long-term use can permanently impair the functioning of the immune system, leaving the body vulnerable to attack.

While my intestinal symptoms continued unabated, throughout the rest of the 1980's, they did not progress much at all. What progressed were my esophageal symptoms, inflammation, pain, ulceration, and congestion, leading to difficulty talking, swallowing, breathing, and sleeping. These symptoms became acute at times, resulting in virtually total disability.

We finally decided to try the two drugs that had made my mother's symptoms bearable all these years, an anti-inflammatory known as Azulfidine and low-dosage steroids, under carefully controlled conditions. Both were to have dangerous side effects for me.

I had read that Azulfidine has side effects. According to the medical literature, it produces depression, nausea, and occasional allergic problems in some people. Unfortunately, I proved to be one of those ''some people'' and was allergic to Azulfidine. In a matter of days, I had broken out in a heavy rash, was alternating chills and fever, and felt completely spaced out. Peggy talked me into going to the hospital and I am lucky that she did. I arrived at the hospital with almost no liver function. I was snapped out of the reaction with a megadose of Decadron. Curiously, the same medication that snapped me out of an allergic reaction also relieved my Crohn's symptoms (which were in essence an allergic reaction to myself). Whenever my symptoms were nearly overwhelming, decadron seemed to be able to bring me back by neutralizing the insidious role of my own immune system.

I was very weak from my latest reversal and was told in no uncertain terms by my internist not to try to attend our older daughter's graduation from Smith College in Northampton, Massachusetts, for which Peggy and our younger daughter had already departed. Thankfully, our sixteen-year old son was able to act as my caretaker to and from Northampton. It was a very special occasion for the whole family. Our namesake, John Kenneth Galbraith, gave the commencement address and told the graduates, "It's not enough for you to do well. You have to do good."

Low-dosage Decadron saw me through acute symptoms in the early 1990's, and I seemed to require it more and more frequently. I have fond recollections of a day at Deer Valley, Utah, skiing with Peggy, followed by a carefree evening together. I recall the day I flew back east with my daughter when she transferred mid-year to Smith, and having a wonderful wintry experience with her. I especially remember a Father's Day gathering, with family basketball games and a backyard picnic. There was a *deja vu* quality to these experiences, harking back to healthier and happier times.

It was such a seductive option to try to take Decadron regularly and see if I could lead a more normal existence, like my mother. But low dosages seemed ineffectual. In

1992, we tried increasing the dosage and, for a few weeks, I thought I was going to have my old energized, productive life back. But steroids can break your heart. I began sleeping very little, gaining lots of weight, and feeling robot-like. I felt I was really sliding. Gary Gitnick and my internist reviewed my experience on the drug and decided to take me off of it, but gradually, because it can otherwise impair adrenal gland function.

Coming off Decadron proved just as eventful as going on. I kept gaining weight, experienced massive and painful muscle spasms, and was just as spacey as before. I spent a year losing the twenty pounds I gained in six weeks on Decadron.

Dehydration was never mentioned to me as a serious risk to Crohn's patients, but it should have been. In 1993, I had some intestinal bleeding followed by a vigorous physical workout (staying in shape was and is a constant battle) and did not replace enough fluids. By lunch time, Peggy and I were joining friends and I felt myself fading out of consciousness. "I'm really sorry," I stammered, "but I don't think I'm going to make it." I meant through lunch.

Peggy saw that I was as white as a sheet and pronounced, "I'm taking you to the hospital." I protested, but she insisted.

"I've felt this way lots of times," I argued. "I just need to go home and lie down. Besides, I can't stand waiting around the Emergency."

We compromised and headed for my internist's office, where I somehow made it up the elevator. He took my blood pressure, or attempted to, and announced that it was "sixty over I can't get a number." He suspected that I was in shock due to dehydration and decided I should go to the Emergency Room by ambulance, even though it was only

a few blocks away. On the way to the hospital, the paramedic yelled to the driver that my blood pressure was only
"Eighty over sixty!" I lay there in a curiously calm state,
more like a spectator than a participant. I wanted to tell
the paramedic, "Don't worry. That's a big improvement
over the last ten minutes."

Soon, they had me on an I.V. and I was recovering. In
fact, once I felt out of danger, I insisted that I would be
fine and did not want to be admitted into the hospital for
observation once I was stabilized. My years of experience
had led me to believe that hospitals are for mandatory
acute care and otherwise are not particularly safe or
healthy places to be. But, thank God, Peggy did get me to
the hospital. It was the second time in two years she had
gotten me there in the nick of time.

Crohn's has had its way with me. Its symptoms run
the gamut and I have experienced most of them. Oddly,
each seems to require its own medical specialty for treatment. Chronic inflammation affects the lens of the eye, so
I have had both of my lenses replaced with plastic ones
by an eye surgeon who is also my good friend. Arthritic
symptoms have resulted in the need for a rheumatologist.
He has been monitoring the possibility that I may also be
suffering from ankylosing spondylitis, a stiffening of the
spine that afflicts some Crohn's patients. He's also monitoring sacroiliitis, a painful inflammation of the joint between the hip and the tailbone known to many Crohn's
sufferers. I also experienced an odd variety of skin rashes,
one of which primarily affected the lower legs, which I assumed must be unrelated. The dermatologist indicated,
however, that these skin eruptions might involve an allergic reaction to my own sweat and treated it with a steroid
cream. I also experienced duodenal ulcers in the section

of the small intestine near the stomach. These ulcers were located by means of an endoscope, a flexible probe that goes from the mouth through the esophagus and stomach. These were easily treated with a common anti-ulcer drug. The increased risk of prostate and colon cancer has involved a urologist, who also saw me through two excruciatingly painful kidney stones, another common symptom, due to an increase in uric acid from dehydration. One tumor-like side effect of one of my medications resulted in my seeing an oncologist. In short, I feel as though I have been supporting the medical profession single-handedly!

I have encountered some other unusual symptoms as part of my seemingly chain-reaction condition, but which may not be directly related to Crohn's. My body became a virtual human thermostat. For years, I have kept my space at home and the office around 70° (my administrative assistant swears it is 60°!) and have had air blowing around the clock. If the temperature rises even a few degrees, or the air stops moving, I get clammy and slightly nauseated. This also happens if I have heat blowing on me, even if the temperature is otherwise fine. I have never had a good explanation of what this is all about, but I often get the reaction, "It's freezing in here!" Maybe it is the wind chill effect of the fan.

I have had an extreme sensitivity to light for years, which I first noticed in my college tennis days. I have since worn sunglasses and a visor when I walk, even on a relatively overcast day. When I sit in a restaurant at lunch, I always face away from the window because otherwise I cannot clearly see my luncheon guest. This problem worsened when I had to have my lenses surgically removed because the plastic implants lack the built-in filter of the human lens. Oddly, this problem is identified in medical literature as a problem with lupus but not often with Crohn's.

As my symptoms progressed, I became more focused on the various options available to me in pursuing the return of my good health, or at least in learning to live with my chronic symptoms. I was bound and determined to make a difference in my own medical care.

II

BEING A
PRO-ACTIVE PATIENT

Peggy and I learned not to be passive patients. We also found that the best doctors listened very well to information that only the patient can provide. They sometimes did not like my cross-examining style, but it was my only way of insuring that we understood each other. If patients remain silent when they have input that could alter a diagnosis or a medication, they do themselves and the doctor a disservice.

As I became a more pro-active patient, I began to try to piece things together from my medical history that could conceivably cast light on the causes or onset of my symptoms. I kept coming back to apthous ulcers. I had experienced similar ulcerations in my mouth at age 6 (we

called them canker sores), which used to make it difficult
to play the trumpet. I used to apply Campho Phenique to
the area, which mostly just smelled up the area around
me. I had these ulcerations on and off for years.

At age twenty-one, I had my first apthous ulcer in the
back of the throat. Because everyone always said ulcers
were caused by stress, I assumed it was because my soon-
to-be fiance, Peggy, had left on a trip to Europe with her
family. No doctor seemed to know how to treat these ulcers and I saw several over the years. One doctor thought
they were the result of a food allergy and put me through
a battery of tests. Everyone emphasized the importance
of gargling with salt water, later antibiotics, and finally
Decadron. One doctor burned out the ulcers with silver
nitrate sticks. This sometimes made things far worse and
left even greater tissue damage.

One of my early "shotgun" treatments for apthous ulcers was a combination of B-12 shots and chicken pox vac-
cinations. I recall seeing the father of a college classmate
in the waiting room, who was being treated for shingles
with the exact same treatment. Shingles can be triggered
by immuno-suppressive drugs. I also learned of some shingles complications in lupus from Joanna Baumer Permut's
book *Embracing the Wolf* (*lupus* means "wolf" in Latin,
which refers to the wolf-like mask that appears around the
eyes of lupus patients in the form of a rash). I keep won-
dering whether all of this will ever fit together into a nice
neat picture, but today it remains blurred.

I eventually saw some throat specialists for relief of apthous ulcers. Despite the myriad of accepted treatments,
the truth is none of them worked, and doctors who had
seen very serious ulceration problems knew it. It must be
difficult for a physician not to be able to heal his patient,
and after awhile a doctor can become jaded. I saw such

a doctor, who tried unsuccessfully to help me. When I returned to his office to have him check on another "episode," I found him unsympathetic and impersonal. It was almost like his asking, "why are you here when you know I can't do anything for you?"

The question for patients and doctors alike was what role these ulcers played in Crohn's symptoms, if any. I wondered if it was the ulceration that provoked the misguided immune reponse and not the healthy, misidentified tissue. We were to discover that this was unlikely.

When the ulcerations worsened, Dr. Gitnick referred me to another throat specialist, who put me on a new drug that would prevent the ulcers from forming. The good news is that the medication is effective against ulcerations. The bad news is that my immune system still attacks the esophagus and the intestine, sometimes unmercifully, and I still occasionally have to break the siege with Decadron. Sometimes, the anti-ulceration medication does not prevent the formation of numerous ulcerations, and I am in for weeks of misery but, thankfully, those times are less frequent now.

A well-meaning pharmacist may have brought on one of the worst sieges I ever experienced, in 1994, when he declined to renew my anti-ulceration prescription. In Gary Gitnick's absence, he spoke to another doctor at UCLA who approved a substitution because the literature disclosed that my medication had resulted in some serious problems in laboratory mice. Unfortunately, the substitute medication proved ineffectual, and I spent the worst two months of my fifteen-year battle with this miserable condition with ulcerations the full length of the esophagus. It turned out that clinical trials with humans had largely discounted the concerns over earlier tests of my medication, and I resumed taking it soon thereafter. Everyone meant well, but it was an example of what can happen when communication breaks down.

There is a great deal you can learn from fellow patients, particularly those close to you. I had seen both my law partner and my sister-in-law remain resilient in the face of the most debilitating symptoms, and I resolved to do the same. My law partner had fought an uphill battle. In 1971, he was given six months to live when tests showed that the melanoma tumor in his leg had metastasized. The cancer doctors at UCLA were using an experimental tuberculosis vaccine called BCG. It produced a high fever that theoretically might kill the cancer cells. Of course, it might also kill the patient. That did not seem to work, so they flew him to Houston to undergo another experimental procedure called a perfusion. The theory was to isolate the leg and run the blood through a machine that would heat it to temperatures the whole body could not tolerate. It was a risky procedure, but his prospects were already pretty grim. He came out of that hellish treatment very weak but determined to pull through. I recall holding on to his hand and telling him to "hang in there" in the recovery room and getting a surprisingly firm squeeze back, although he appeared barely there.

Across the hall, there was another young lawyer with another form of cancer, less serious and at an earlier stage. He had a good chance to recover. But he received a cruel setback in the form of a notice from his firm that his medical benefits had run out and that they could no longer support him. This seemed to cause a dramatic worsening in his condition and he died several weeks later. It was almost as though, if his law partners had given up on him, what was the point in his fighting on? Meanwhile, my law partner went on to have another child and lived some meaningful years.

My sister-in-law had a similar fight in her. Her lupus condition was not widely understood by doctors back in 1964, and she suffered as much from the heavy steroid treatment as from the disease. But she managed to carry on. Because both of us had been avid tennis players, we decided to play in a round robin tournament together. We quickly found ourselves in a 0–3 hole against a good team. I walked over to her and asked, "What do you think?"

"I think we better stop hitting with them and go to the all-court game," she replied, smiling. Basically, she meant that we should neutralize their power with chips and slices, lobs and changes of pace, to keep them off balance. And we should keep them on the run. Her determination in carrying out this strategy told me a lot about her. We ended up winning 6–3, 6–1.

Afterwards, I could see that her ankles and wrists were swollen, and that this had been too much for her. She would never have complained.

I also learned a great deal from my mother's experience with Crohn's disease, though it oddly has not greatly paralleled my own. She was misdiagnosed for years. Because my parents travelled a lot on my father's sabbatical leaves from the UCLA History Department, it was easy to assume that my mother had picked up amoebic dysentery or some exotic condition from places like Kenya, South Africa, India, and other outreaches of the former British Empire.

It strikes me as fascinating that my hereditary condition could not be treated by the drugs that so effectively controlled my mother's symptoms. Also, it is curious that my mother's condition has run the more usual course, with far greater intestinal damage and almost no involvement of the esophagus.

My mother actually had some preliminary symptoms

as early as age twenty-five but did not have her condition definitively diagnosed until her early fifties. Fortunately, she found a doctor with recognized expertise who was able to control her symptoms with reduced dosages of Azulfidine and prednisone, which she took for more than twenty years. By taking prednisone every other day, her doctor reasoned that there would be less likelihood of permanently and dangerously repressing her immune system.

More recently, my mother's case has finally taken a turn for the better. In 1992, she had five hours of surgery to repair years of tissue damage caused by her own immune system. To undergo the surgery, she first went off steroids completely for the first time in over twenty years. The surgery amounted to a complete overhaul, essentially removing damaged tissue and patching together healthy tissue, while shoring up the ligaments and lining that hold the whole intestinal system in place.

Not only did the surgery go well, my mother never resumed her regimen of steroids and Azulfidine. While she still had the residual effects of the condition, she was able to resume a fairly normal life. When she consulted with her physician, she found a logical explanation. Her immune system in her late seventies simply was not as virulent and was not capable of attacking her normal intestinal tissue as savagely. While I surely hope they find a cure in less than twenty-five years, if all else fails I can count on my immune system to start to run out of gas in only a quarter of a century!

I became very curious to learn how Gary Gitnick's similarly-situated patients were faring. Out of respect for patient privacy, Gary told me very little, but that little was a lot. He said that we all had very intense personalities, were very entrepreneurial and competitive, and very pro-active as patients. While all of us had constant esophageal symptoms, none of us had suffered sufficient intestinal damage to require surgery.

I had assumed that stress was a major cause of ulcerations. Gary's characterizations of the personalities of his three patients with throat ulcerations seemed to reinforce this. But then the breakthrough based on the assumption of a common bacterial cause for ulcers produced the miracle medication that virtually prevented ulcers from forming. At present, I have no idea if stress is still considered a major factor.

You can even learn a lot from a patient you have never met. For example, early news reports were that Rolf Benirschke, the place-kicker for the San Diego Chargers, had Crohn's disease, which caught my attention. I followed his progress in the press and was very touched by his television appearance at the center of the field with his teammates soon after recovering from near-fatal complications. He had lost a tremendous amount of weight and leaned on his teammates for support, but he was there, clearly committed to overcoming his affliction and living life.

Later, I learned that all of Benirschke's symptoms had gone away after he underwent a colostomy. I called Gary Gitnick to inquire about this, and wonder if a colostomy would help me. He said that the medical profession was well aware that Bernirschke had ulcerative colitis, which affects only the colon. If the colon is removed, you no longer have ulcerative colitis. Unfortunately, Crohn's symptoms affect tissue throughout the digestive system, except the stomach.

All patients want a clear diagnosis, a specific course of treatment, and relief within a reasonable period. In the case of most chronic illnesses, patients are likely to be disappointed. The best results, however, are obtained when the doctor and patient have an excellent working relationship.

For a doctor to properly treat a patient, the patient has to communicate effectively to the doctor not only his symptoms and his medical history, but his habits, his diet, and his mental state. The patient himself can be the doctor's best resource in deciding on the best course of treatment. In the words of Dr. Albert Schweitzer, "Each patient carries his own doctor inside of him. They come to us not knowing that truth. We are at our best when we give the doctor who resides within each patient a chance to go to work."

Frequently, the process of visiting the doctor's office is stressful because of anxiety over test results or their interpretation, the inevitable waiting period in the reception area, and the doctor's pressed schedule. In that environment, it is hard to recall all the concerns that were weighing on you. In the doctor's office or examination room, the momentum of the appointment normally swings to the doctor's focus and invariably many questions are left unanswered. After a number of such experiences, I began making a list of questions and concerns and taking two copies with me to my appointment, one to leave with the doctor. I was very pleased by the response. Even when the doctor was pressed for time, he appeared to value my participation and to increase his energy level and focus on my concerns. My rheumatologist observed that patients are nervous about asserting themselves, but that a study he had seen found that patients that took an active part in their care received a significantly better level of care and results. I have had the same experience in discussing diagnoses, medication, and recommended medical tests. The more comfortable I became with the doctor and my condition, and the better questions I asked, the more focused my communication was with the doctor.

In more recent years, as a visit to the doctor became more physically difficult for me, I have been faxing a summary of my symptoms and observations to my doctors, generally leaving a message for them to call me at their convenience. This has helped to focus my doctors on my progress without draining my limited physical resources or unduly utilizing the doctor's valuable office time.

Norman Cousins had the first chapter of his book *Anatomy of an Illness* published in the New England Journal of Medicine. Three thousand doctors wrote to him in response. They were not only intrigued by his examination of the beneficial healing effects of laughter, for which Cousins is best remembered, but were receptive to his belief in the importance of a partnership between a physician and his patient in search of a cure. Medical schools now emphasize that good medical practice begins with good listening.

Unfortunately, there is a tendency to shut out your own doctor by telling him you have everything under control. No one wants to sound like a complainer, and surely the doctor is aware of much worse cases. I was fortunate to have Peggy intercede with doctors on my behalf. I recall her writing Gary Gitnick and speaking with him by phone to underscore that I was putting much too favorable a spin on my ongoing symptoms. She, of course, saw me at the worst of my suffering, something a doctor could only try to learn about by listening.

Why would any patient want to minimize his symptoms? I am not certain of the reasons myself, but I believe it has to do with saying it with the will to make it so, with a desire not to be a guinea pig any more, with a resignation that nothing can really be done about it anyway. It may also simply be a desire not to project yourself as a pathetic case, or it may be a sense of duty to the doctor to start getting better in response to the course of treatment he has prescribed based on all his expertise.

Coming to terms with chronic illness is the result of hard work and serious reflection. While it may involve accepting some unwanted limitations, it also opens the mind and the soul to life's potentialities and simple pleasures. Life becomes more precious, with no day to be wasted in self-pity or resignation.

III

RELYING ON
FAMILY AND FRIENDS

Chronic illness affects everyone around you: family, friends, and associates. With the onset of my full range of symptoms in 1979 came the cruelest effect of all: limits. I had always been a high-energy person, taking my greatest pleasure in doing things for those I cared about. Suddenly, I was severely limited in what I could do and that reflected on my relationships. Peggy recalls my not being able to make all the efforts I once made and that she resented it when I appeared to be able to run on adrenaline to make efforts for others. A few years later, we talked about the fact that you cannot run on adrenaline with your most important relationship twenty-four hours a day. On the other hand, we found we could prioritize one-on-one

times where I could be "on" and be able to share feelings
at an intense level. While I could not last through an evening socially, we began accepting invitations just for the
cocktail hour, so we could stay in touch with our friends.
I started scheduling frequent breakfasts with friends and
associates, finding that this was an excellent way for someone who was not really "out there" to stay in touch.

Unless you are chronically ill, or live with someone
who is, it is difficult to comprehend the complications of
a "normal" day. Different conditions produce different
difficulties. In the case of Crohn's disease, different sets
of symptoms will also present different challenges. For
me, just getting up out of a chair is an effort, especially if
I am dealing with intestinal spasming and arthritic flare-
ups. Standing is enervating, again because of the intestinal and arthritic effects. Walking is easier than standing
(it probably is for most people) if arthritic symptoms permit. Sometimes the sacroiliac and hip joints make this too
painful, and often my walk route has to go by my front
door a few times because of the onset of intestinal symptoms. Even short drives to meetings or social occasions are
difficult because it is part of a period of "on" time, where
I have to make the effort to deal with logistics, keep my
symptoms at bay, and be at my best for people time. Most
often, I have to run on adrenaline to make it through these
times.

Normally, intestinal, arthritic, and esophageal symptoms make it difficult to sleep for long periods at a time.
Although I have no difficulty going to sleep, the arthritic
pain necessitates not staying in one position, the intestinal symptoms often get me up, and an inflamed esophagus makes breathing and sleeping uncomfortable.

When any of these symptoms is acute, there is no

normal day. It is enough just to make it through the day, perhaps dealing with a few personal and professional emergencies. If the symptoms reach crisis proportions, and they rarely do, we head to the hospital.

Sadly, many of the chronically ill face far worse symptoms and a far more dire prognosis. They must overcome so much more than I. Also, many of the physically disabled face much more difficult logistical problems in dealing with their day. No matter the seriousness of the symptoms of the prognosis, or the logistical difficulties, we must deal with our conditions as we find them, seeking to make the adjustments necessary to establish for ourselves what we can reasonably expect from our "normal" days.

These limitations and hindrances affect everyone around you as your deficiencies become other people's burdens. Out of town business trips, all-day or evening meetings are assigned to others. Shopping trips, cross-town pickups, lengthy, distant, or late-evening social events, camping trips, sporting events, and other fixtures of normal life, must be left to others. Fortunately, my family members have not had to lessen their involvements and activities. In turn, I have increased my reading, writing, corresponding, telephoning, and observing life. It is not a worse existence, other than the physical symptoms, only different.

My being at home in the afternoons created a new family dynamic. My children were ages thirteen, eleven, and eight in 1981. My relationship with them may actually have been enhanced by my confinement at home, except when acute symptoms separated me from them. I was generally home with them, and for them, and loved their comfort in talking with me about anything, anytime. Of course, they all went through their adolescent years when my opinions were not valued nor sought, but, all in all, I feel those growing up years were very special.

Our children went to a school nearby, which prioritized participation in sports, drama, and music. It made it easy for me to come and go, to be in touch with what they were doing. I could no longer be as actively involved, as I was with six years of coaching their AYSO soccer teams when they were younger, but I was there on the periphery.

Despite my increasing difficulty with travel, I stubbornly persevered for years. There were just so many places I wanted to go with my family, so many wonderful experiences we could share together. We used to ski in Aspen, a destination that literally takes all day to get to from Los Angeles, unless you're willing to risk the dive-bomb into Aspen Airport in a commuter or private plane. We always took the long way, landing first in Denver, then Grand Junction, and driving the remaining two hours.

For some reason, it only took about three inches of snow to close Denver's Stapleton Airport. They just never seem to have adequate snow removal equipment. On one of our trips, we were snowed in at Stapleton, unable to get to Grand Junction where our rental car was and where our baggage was evidently about to be shipped. It looked like we would be spending the night at the airport. I was standing in line seeking assistance. Peggy asked me, "Do you think we can find a way out of here?"

I pointed to a man in front of me in a Pendleton shirt. "Do you know who that is? If John Glenn's snowed in, we're probably snowed in, too!"

But fortune smiled on us. I found my way into the inner sanctum of Stapleton and talked to one of the baggage handlers. I said I had a health problem and needed to get eighteen bags off the flight to Grand Junction (which for some reason could make it with bags but not passengers) and to get us all on a bus to Aspen in twenty-five minutes. This very large-bodied and big-hearted man got us on the bus with minutes to spare.

I would soon question my sanity. It is a four-hour bus trip from Denver to Aspen, and we left near midnight. With all of our ski paraphernalia and smaller bags, we were packed in like sardines. I had increasing inflammation throughout the trip and realized explosive intestinal symptoms were not far off. I began looking forward more to a clean bathroom than to a ski paradise.

Another abortive trip to Aspen resulted in our being re-routed to Las Vegas because, naturally, Stapleton was closed. We had planned to spend our first Christmas morning away from home in a wintry wonderland. Instead, we checked into a nondescript hotel off the Strip. Everyone around us looked like they had been drinking and gambling around the clock and probably had. No one seemed to know it was Christmas Eve. Peggy somehow managed to make Christmas morning special, leaving packages outside the door of the children's room, and gathering us together for a family breakfast. Suddenly, we received a call that we were being bused back to the airport to make another attempt to land at Stapleton.

For someone who has only a few good hours a day, these kinds of logistics are impossible. I suffered severe flare-ups on both these trips, and we resolved to try Deer Valley, Utah, in the future because Salt Lake City International Airport knows how to deal with winter weather.

My last trip out of the country in 1983 was a calculated

risk, and I lost. We travelled to Scotland to visit relatives (my father was born in Glasgow) and to travel the countryside. I loved introducing Peggy and the children to my Aunt Mary McCrone. She served tea and enchanted us all with her Scottish brogue and her family stories. I wish I could pronounce my own name the way she does: "Gal-bra-ith," with the accent on the middle syllable (it only has two syllables my way and is a lot less lyrical).

Unfortunately, I became increasingly and violently sick and had to return home, with the considerable assistance of British Airways. I needed to be near my own doctors and my own hospitals. I also needed my usual schedule, regimen, and diet to best regulate my symptoms. Happily, the family was able to finish the trip without me.

Looking back, I do not regret making these and numerous other trips during the 1980's. I used to say, in fact, that "I've been sick in some pretty nice places!"

After sixteen years of increasingly difficult symptoms, I do not travel much anymore. Except for an occasional weekend trip to the local mountains, my only travel is ninety miles by freeway to La Jolla, to visit my parents and my sister's family, a few times a year. I am truly grateful for my considerable opportunity to travel in earlier years and am pleased to see Peggy venturing out more without me. The children are all grown now and are free to travel the world.

I have been blessed by a wonderful family. Peggy is an extraordinary person who has picked up my slack the past several years. Our children have worked hard and are poised to live productive, happy lives. They have seen that life can present you with great fortune and dire affliction and that what is most important is what you make of it.

I do worry about the hereditary tendency of Crohn's

disease and hope there will be some dramatic progress in its treatment, or even a cure, before any of them reach their middle thirties, the most common age of onset of symptoms.

Every time my three children have intestinal symptoms or a sore throat, they have to wonder whether this may be the precursor of Crohn's symptoms. Each of them has at one time or another asked "Just how hereditary is it?" I have explained that someone with a parent who has Crohn's is thirty to forty times more likely to get it than someone from the general population. Because only about 200,000 are diagnosed with Crohn's in the U.S., that is about one in 1200. If the odds are forty times greater, my children's chances should only be one in thirty (I suppose it is one in ten that one of the three will get it). It is not like some conditions that are one in two or one in four. Still, it remains a worry for them.

It was my good fortune to have my older daughter marry an outstanding young man with plans to become a doctor. He has taken a sincere interest in my case and helped me to focus on my own symptoms in an analytical way. He was, in fact, the one who traced my renewed ulceration problem to the switch in my medication, and explained to me why the old prescription was more effective.

Our family had a lot to deal with as my illness progressed. I had to direct most of my energy to recovering and could not, at first, be as responsive to Peggy and our three children. The children had their own anxieties, mostly unspoken.

My initial denial and eventual anger was intense. My family had to feel at times that my anger was directed at them personally. They were left to deal with the unknown. How would this affect life as they had known it?

Would they get sick, too? Was their husband/father going to die, like Dad's law partner or Mom's sister? How could they be helpful? How would expectations of them change?

Inevitably, my feelings of guilt for being sick, or for allowing or causing myself to become sick, were shared by Peggy and perhaps by the children. It is important that the rest of the family can separate the patient from the illness and close ranks around the patient, so that they can work together to address family concerns and priorities.

They had to blame me, or at least my condition, for leaving them vulnerable and for restricting the family's financial and logistical options. As years passed, it may have actually increased everyone's resolve to be self-sufficient.

Peggy bore the greatest burden during my lengthy battle to overcome chronic illness. She dealt with it as if it were "our" illness. As I moved through the states of denial, anger, isolation, depression, reconstruction, and rehabilitation discussed by JoAnn LeMaistre, Ph.D., in her book *Beyond Rage* (and not necessarily in that simple an order), Peggy went through them, too. She has always been a highly-sensitive person, which proves to be both a blessing and a curse around someone who is chronically ill. She felt everything I was going through, which is difficult, even vicariously. She worked through my shock and inability to accept or deal with my early symptoms. She sidestepped my anger and tried not to assume that I was angry with her. She sensed my isolation, and felt frozen out herself at times. She was depressed by my depression and was usually the one to pull me out of it. She made the reconstruction of our life patterns and priorities into a joint undertaking and heaved a sigh of relief as I finally seemed able to begin to rehabilitate myself both physically and emotionally.

Peggy recalls my resolutely concluding, after perhaps a year of symptoms, that I had finally come to grips
with chronic illness. In fact, I had no idea what I was up
against, no concept of how to deal with it, and inadequate
emotional and intellectual tools with which to work. I had
not even started the process in any meaningful way, let
alone finished it. Perhaps twelve years into the process,
I reached the point that the prospects of rehabilitation
were promising. Peggy was able to understand better than
I how to get on with life, seeing her need to be much
stronger and more independent. She became more actively involved in our business affairs, took on positions
of leadership with community organizations, and kept in
good touch with her own support group of friends. She
started a program of fitness that made her stronger,
healthier, and more resilient. She read more, took classes
in music and literature, went to the symphony and the
opera with friends, and took trips with the children to
Africa and to Italy. She also went camping with them at
Tuolumne Meadows (in Yosemite National Park), a trip
we all went on with friends in previous years. She took
over the principal role in entertaining our friends, with my
role becoming sort of a cameo appearance.

She never caved-in to the pressures and difficulties of
living with a chronically-ill spouse, although I know there
had to be times when she was at her wit's end. She had
to ask "why us?" and to question life's lack of fairness.
Oddly enough, that unspoken question has led to an amazing transformation in her outlook on life. She now is so
grateful for the life we have and the different life we have
yet to experience. She cherishes even more our family and
friends, her own health, and the opportunities for growth
that have opened up to her.

I have known Peggy for thirty-two years, of which we

have been married twenty-nine. She was an extraordinary person at nineteen, but I do not believe she knew she was until recent years. It was not false modesty. She just had incredibly high standards and judged herself harshly against them. I am most fortunate indeed to have the chance to appreciate her over the years and to grow with her in the years to come.

In order for any family to avoid becoming prisoners of the patient's condition, they need to communicate their thoughts, feelings, and fears. How they are able to do this will depend on how well they dealt with difficulties and differences in the past. I feel very blessed by how well my family has handled this.

In the stage of reconstruction, you become more receptive to ideas from family and friends. You are more able to play an active role in creating your life beyond chronic illness and your adaptive relationships with family and friends. This requires great flexibility, because these relationships cannot be what they were or be burdened by what they could have been. They have to be based on the here and now and on what can be.

Both Peggy's family and mine have been very supportive. In order for me to be able to make my "cameo" appearances at holiday occasions, we have large family gatherings at our home three or four times a year, and our families make the effort to converge from all over Southern California. These are very special three-generation celebrations, which give us a wonderful sense of family solidarity.

My common affliction with my mother has brought us even closer together. The symptoms of Crohn's are so bizarre that it is difficult for anyone to truly empathize with what you are going through without having experienced them. We have shared intestinal symptoms, arthritic symptoms, lens replacements, exasperation with the medical bureaucracy, pleasure at establishing a relationship with the right specialist, and disappointment at the lack of progress in medical research.

My father was never sick and treated cold and flu symptoms with contempt. He did not have time for them. He was busy writing and teaching the history of the 19th century British Empire. My mother's illness was particularly difficult for him because it was so unspecific in its early stages. This is true of many auto-immune diseases and is what makes them all the more insidious. During those times you are able to overcome the pain, the nausea, the creakiness, the exhaustion, and the depression, people think you look just fine. Well, my father thought my mother looked fine, too. It wasn't until she had experienced years of symptoms that doctors identified that she had Crohn's disease. I think both my mother and father were relieved to have something more specific to be dealing with. Years later, my mother confessed that it was not until I was diagnosed with Crohn's that she finally stopped feeling like a malingerer and a hypochondriac around my father.

In recent years, my father has encountered some medical problems of his own, which have made him profoundly more empathetic with what I am going through and with what my mother went through for so many years. His empathy and his supportive interest has meant a great deal to me.

Close friends and family do learn how to monitor you and it is a special gift when they are able to read your condition and needs. At a gala celebration honoring our younger daughter, I had been running on empty all evening and was stubbornly trying to make it through the evening. As I waltzed my younger daughter across the floor and delivered her to her escort, I sensed I was going to pass out right there. A close friend was suddenly at my side, holding me up. "You need to go, don't you?" I nodded, and minutes later he had me on my way home.

There are times in life when you simply have to be there for family and friends, no matter how badly you are doing physically. The day of my older daughter's wedding I was determined to make it through without incident, despite experiencing physical difficulties. I slept in the afternoon before the wedding, and it went off without a hitch. By the time we arrived home from the reception, I was having increased symptoms. But it was imperative to carry on. Peggy arranged things so I could greet our guests sitting down. The evening was magical, and our daughter and her husband and their friends had such a *joi-de vivre*. I was eventually overwhelmed by physical symptoms and had to retreat back to the house while the party was still going. It was not tragic, only too bad.

Illness can burden friendships. Some changes are to be expected if you cannot fit into old patterns, such as trips and late night gatherings. But there's also an unease, even among some close friends, about illness. It somehow changes the chemistry, or there may even be a fear that the condition is contagious. Happily, it appears impossible to transmit Crohn's disease other than through hereditary predisposition. So, my wife, my friends and my associates have nothing to fear.

Chronically-ill patients can make it difficult on friends. I know I have. When someone wants to be upbeat, they say things like "You look terrific!" Unfortunately, when you are not feeling "terrific," this does not bring you closer to your friend. Others, who know you better or are used to being around those with health problems, might say "I wish you felt as good as you look," or "If your eyes weren't such a give-away, I would think you were doing better." Those who know me best can tell just from my eyes and mouth whether I am in a "reprieve" (in which I briefly feel okay) or if I am grimly holding on. My eyes are the windows of my soul. If they are without spark and are surrounded by deep, dark sockets, the chances are that this is not one of my better moments. If my mouth is a thin line and my jaw is clenched, it is likely I am not feeling too well.

As the chronically ill learn to cope better with our conditions, we have a responsibility to help our friends with their acts of friendship. To those who say you look great, you can say "looking well is the best revenge," or "thanks, but you should see what I look like on the inside." It depends on the occasion and the circumstances whether you or your friend want your health to be any more of a topic than that.

Friends will naturally want to help and will want you to appreciate their help, but you will not be able to follow everyone's suggestions, even at the risk of hurting people's feelings. Often, you will not have the physical or emotional stamina to dilute your current course of treatment. At the same time, you have to be forever vigilant for ideas that may prove beneficial.

One of my closest friends wanted me to go to the Mayo Clinic because of its world-famous gastroenterology department. I was having trouble just making it to a local internist at that time and was confident in Gary Gitnick's expertise. My failure to visit Mayo made my friend feel as though I was not letting him help me. Finally, I relented and said I would call Mayo and was glad I did. After a brief inquiry into my course of treatment, I was asked who

I was seeing for the condition. When I said Gary Gitnick, the reaction was unequivocal:

"Well, you're seeing the best. He had a fellowship here at Mayo and we have no one here who could provide better care."

I was relieved to have finally been responsive to my friend, to be seeing the best, and to be spared a long trip to Rochester, Minnesota.

Other suggestions from friends were harder to follow. I was asked to consider secret herbal remedies, green tea, vitamin therapy, a liquid diet, vegetarianism, more active intestinal bacterial cultures, colonic irrigation, Christian Science, and Transcendental Meditation. Some of these suggestions may have merit, perhaps all of them. Some overlap with approaches I have taken or am pursuing. Everyone's suggestions are appreciated.

A discouraging and frequent development for me is to gear my entire day around meaningful people interaction for an hour or so and yet still be unable to function, even semi-normally. I make the effort because family, friend, and associate relationships are truly important to me. If I arrive at the appointed hour in pain and discomfort, and therefore not smiling or relaxed, I feel disappointed that the person for whom I made the effort cannot really know, with the exception of family and a few very close friends who can read me like a book.

Friends try to empathize. Those with strep throat, the flu, or even intestinal irregularity have often told me "I don't know how you deal with this all the time." The secret is, of course, *not* to deal with it but to redirect your focus and your energy. Only when I am going to have quality people time do I try to mask my symptoms, so they will not interfere. This, of course, is impossible if the symptoms are acute.

I have had the pleasure of being associated with a large number of partners over the years. I have always broken the rule "never do business with friends," though I recognize that business setbacks can sorely test friendships. My principal partner the past fifteen years was my friend and tennis partner for a dozen years before that. He was also briefly a client before I stopped practicing law and was the person with whom I launched my entrepreneurial career in 1979.

The choice of a partner had been an important one. I had felt a sense of confidence in my experience with the "non-operating" side of business, involving such matters as insurance, real estate, accounting, financing, government regulation, labor conflicts, and general legal issues. What I felt I needed was a partner who understood the "operating" side of business, someone with executive management experience who knew how to produce products "better, cheaper, faster." My long-time friend, with a sophisticated management and engineering background, filled that bill and was enthusiastic about joining forces. By allocating areas of responsibility, I felt I could handle my end of the bargain. Our entrepreneurial involvements, however, were to have a life force of their own.

My long-time friend and partner seemed to suffer vicariously with me and had an ability to "read" my physical condition. Our agonies and ecstasies the past fifteen years forged an even deeper friendship. I doubt that would have been possible if he could not empathize with my situation.

I had two important partners in the early 1980's, who I had not known well but who were friends of friends. They were indispensably involved in helping my principal partner and me meet some of our biggest challenges. But they never really knew me or what I was going through, which probably made some of our crises more difficult to resolve.

You may be surprised by which friendships strengthen and which slowly slip away in the face of chronic illness. There is generally unanimous support at a perceived moment of crisis, but as that passes many friends may be unable or unwilling to deal with the realities of your situation. They may feel rejected by your anger, disgusted by your helplessness, brought down by your depression, overwhelmed by your symptoms, or they may just not want to be reminded of their own vulnerability and mortality. For some, it may be more cold—they simply may not feel you are an asset to them any longer.

It is your family and your true friends who will see you through the long and winding road of chronic illness. As soon as you are able, you must help them help you and remove some of their burden. Through this process, you may conclude as I have that the most important measure of your life is the assemblage of your personal relationships. If you are miraculously cured but still find yourself alone out there, your life will have little meaning. Conversely, if the rest of your life is a physical struggle but your family and friends help you separate your physical from your psychological and philosophical self, you will have a life rich with possibilities.

IV

SEEKING ALTERNATIVE APPROACHES

There is a range of responses available to the chronically-ill patient. At one extreme, you can be resigned, helpless, and construe your condition as somehow your fault. Conversely, you can tell the world you are completely fine and have everything under control. Neither approach is likely to help you deal with your situation and both approaches will distance you from those who truly care about you and want to help. With their help, you can begin to adjust psychologically to the reality of your physical problems. While it may seem obvious to a healthy person that one's self worth transcends any physical difficulty, it is not so clear to someone new to physical

limitations. You start questioning yourself as a person because of what you suddenly cannot do. Each person will
deal with this on a very individualized basis. If your relationships with your friends have revolved around the golf
course or the tennis court, and you are no longer able to
participate, it will unavoidably affect those relationships.
In some instances, the lack of access to friends will create distance. In others, efforts by you and your friends will
forge new common ground and renewed, and even deep-
ened, relationships.

The adjustments and transitions in your relationships
with family, friends, and associates will not be smooth or
integrated. Everyone will adjust differently and at different paces. As a result, the overall adjustment process is
lengthy, unpredictable, filled with anxiety, and exhausting emotionally as well as physically.

One of the biggest challenges of the chronically ill is
uncertainty. In designing an alternative vocational plan,
you cannot know whether your health will permit you to
carry it through or for how long. But, then, no one's future is ever guaranteed. You simply have to accept a
higher anxiety level than others.

There is no question that the prospect of diminished
physical capacity can be depressing. I found dealing with
this to be greatly assisted by therapy. It got out on the ta-
ble feelings that my instinct was to repress. I felt anxiety,
fear, anger, and a real sense of loss. I felt wonderful support from family and friends, but I did not know my own
needs, which made it very difficult for them to help.

My therapy sessions revealed a deep sense of guilt on
my part about being sick. In my subconscious mind, I felt
that I had set myself up for a medical collapse by literally
burning it at both ends for years. Starting in law school,
and for twenty years thereafter, I had averaged only about

five hours of sleep nightly. I prided myself on being there for my family, friends, and associates, and my community, and on "working hard, playing hard."

When my internist first advised me to slow down, I shrugged off his advice, truly believing I could take anything in stride. That headstrong and arrogant stance, of course, masked a powerful "fear of failure" on my part. It was not that I believed I could not fail, professionally or personally, it was that I had no idea how to cope with such a failure.

Those family and friends who understand the confusion you feel and steadfastly stand by you until they can comfortably be helpful or supportive are a treasure. It is not easy to be a friend to someone dealing with such a jumble of emotions and physical distress.

Eventually and mercifully, an equilibrium replaces the chaos. The future course of the illness is better understood, and the economic and practical consequences to the family are better adjusted to. Relationships have had time to adjust. You have had time to modify your physical existence, rather than dwelling on what used to be or could have been.

In our rush to become well, patients are psychologically prepared to have any medical treatment work. In the early stages of practically every medication I took (and there were dozens over fifteen years), there was a temporary euphoria, most often followed by a letdown. Either the medication was not as effective as hoped or the side effects neutralized the benefits. I expect that the placebo effect was responsible for much of the euphoria. If you believe something will help you, it will up to a point.

Western medicine, including doctors and patients, seems fixated on drugs. While there are, of course, miracle medications that preserve the quality of patients' lives, there are also those that simply mask symptoms or obliterate patients' consciousness. If Americans are sedated, they may not feel the full effects of their symptoms, but they may not feel much else either. In the early stages of my medical nightmare, I eagerly sought relief from my myriad of symptoms. In the words of Huey Lewis, for every symptom, I needed "a new drug." There were drugs that reduced nausea, diarrhea, bloating, pain and inflammation, drugs that inhibited intestinal spasming and the muscle spasms due to withdrawal from steroids, drugs that eased skin rashes, drugs that reduced the congestion from throat inflammation, drugs that reduced bone and muscle inflammation. All of them served a purpose, but once you have thrown in additional drugs to alleviate the side-effects, you can no longer function as a human being. Today, I regularly take only one prescription medication to prevent throat ulceration, and occasionally aspirin and Actifed to reduce the pain and congestion from inflammation.

There are other medical professionals besides physicians. I have found needed relief from chiropractic, acupuncture, physical therapy, physical training, massage therapy, psychological therapy, dietary consultation, and spiritual healing, which I discuss in a later chapter.

A good chiropractor can help save your body from the law of gravity. An erect posture and well-balanced muscles to hold the skeleton in place are essential to good physical condition. Occasional readjustment and realigning of the skeletal structure has provided me a great deal of relief over the years.

My chiropractor's own experience with a broken back led him into a chiropractic career. A fall down the stairs left him with three compression fractures of the vertebrae. A battery of orthopedists and neurologists advised him it would be too dangerous to operate because of the risk of paralysis, and that he would just have to learn to live with the pain. But he could not stand for long enough periods to continue teaching and had to go on disability leave. Then he discovered chiropractic and physical training and a year later he was virtually without pain.

I am a true believer in acupuncture. I had a pinched nerve that caused incessant pain, from which I could find no relief. My massage therapist referred me to a Chinese practitioner of acupuncture. She spent a good deal of time seeing to it that I was in a calm physical and emotional state before beginning her treatment. She heated the acupuncture needles in a solution treated with a Chinese herb my children laughingly said smelled like marijuana. I felt little pain on insertion of the needles. I was reduced to an almost suspended state for quite an extended time. Finally, she woke me and asked if I still felt the pain. Astonishingly, I felt none for several hours. In the ensuing days, it receded completely.

Physical therapy and physical training are invaluable. Therapy is to help rehabilitate muscles weakened by inflammation or lack of use and to restore a normal range of motion. Training is to build strength and endurance. While they are separate functions, they both require professionals with substantial physiological training and experience. The wrong program can actually hurt you physically and prolong your recovery.

Massage is a blessing to your muscles. It can reduce tightness, spasming, tension. It also promotes mental, as well as physical, relaxation. It also often provides the rejuvenation of a daytime nap, which served the likes of Thomas Edison, Winston Churchill, and John Kennedy so well. I find it allows me a fresh perspective on the pressing issues of the day.

In 1979, dietary fiber was a major focus of the medical profession in treating Crohn's disease. It makes sense that ulcerated and inflamed intestinal tissue would not respond well to a high fiber diet. The irritation would undoubtedly cause pain, and in fact it did. But my own experience with diet was that, while I could monitor fiber and therefore regulate pain, the overall course of my symptoms did not seem to be materially affected by diet. When I commented on this to my internist, it seemed surprising and perhaps unscientific to him. When I repeated it to Gary Gitnick a few years later, though, he said that many patients felt the same way and he agreed that the benefits of a "white" (low fiber) diet had to be weighed against increased nausea and decreased intestinal function.

Throughout the 1980's, I did daily floor exercises, walked about a mile and a half per day, and played tennis once or twice a week. As my arthritic symptoms progressed in the early 1990's, I had to cut back on this regimen, though I am struggling to increase it again. I have consistently found that exercise energizes me and empowers me to face my symptoms and life's other challenges.

Tennis has long been my obsession, as well as a means of exercise. After badly tearing the ligaments in my right shoulder in 1968, I stubbornly continued to play, with shorter and shorter backswings and follow-throughs. I finally gave it up in 1980 due to sharp pain and increasing medical problems. But, in 1983, I began taking lessons left-handed and resumed playing with my previous enthusiasm, albeit with reduced skill.

My secret weapon on the court was Peggy. While her sister was well recognized for her junior tennis exploits, with a number two national ranking, Peggy was a fine player and a wonderful partner. She taught me a lot about life on the tennis court.

For a few years, tennis was a joy for me. I looked forward to Thursday morning doubles matches and Sunday morning lessons. I felt I was re-learning the game, although I never got over thinking right-handed. Then, a new problem arose—I could not see the ball. My vision in my dominant left eye went from 20/20 to 20/600 over a period of several months due to a cataract, evidently occasioned by systemic inflammation. I would watch an opponent's swing and headed for where I thought the ball would be. And then it would come into view, leaving little reaction time. Successful implantation of a plastic lens inside the eyball magically solved the problem. Soon thereafter, the procedure had to be repeated with my right lens.

But intense sacroiliac and hip pain, even treated with strong anti-inflammatories, created new problems. I could not pivot, especially to the right. If I leaned forward and to the right, I frequently ended up sprawling on the court. As a result, serving an ace to my right became almost a free point for my opponents, who humored me except when they really needed a point! In 1993, my arthritic symptoms finally forced me off the court temporarily.

I am now working on another comeback. I am patterning my game after the Huntington Hotel tennis pro for fifty years, who played into his nineties. He never seemed to move, but he was always in the right place. My tennis partner is going to have to cover a lot of court!

Inflammation in the throat leads understandably to unconscious shallow breathing, which leads sometimes to oxygen deprivation and nausea. At night it can awake me. Deep breathing is an obvious solution. Intestinal pain also can be dealt with by short, focused breathing, which I borrowed from Peggy's Lamaze classes years ago.

Visualization and utilization of "the relaxation response," popularized by Herbert Benson, M.D., author of the book by the same name, are very valuable tools in freeing the body and mind of the stress caused by chronic pain. This also involves slow, deep breathing. A mind over body technique, also involving visualization, is particularly good at focusing you into a positive attitude. The power of positive thinking and the power of suggestion are remarkable forces in the healing process. The effectiveness of biofeedback is evidence of this. The mind can control the pulse, body temperature, blood pressure, and other body indices. Surely, it can also control and even reverse disease.

I looked into support groups sponsored by the National Foundation for Ileitis and Colitis (Crohn's disease most often affects the colon and the ileum, the portion of the small intestine adjoining the colon). I chose not to join one because I was having difficulty even making it to doctors' appointments and did not think I could attend evening meetings far from home. Instead, I reached out to everyone I knew with the disease and was receptive to talking with friends of friends who were dealing with Crohn's. One young woman felt her diagnosis with Crohn's had shattered her life. Her fiance could not deal with her symptoms and called off the wedding. She was trying to learn to adjust to her condition, while at the same time putting her life back together.

The several Crohn's sufferers I spoke to, mostly by telephone, were younger and had only been recently diagnosed. They were still in the early stages of shock, denial, and anger. It seemed to provide some comfort to most of them to know I still had a life after many years with the disease. My mother has been able to provide me that same comfort.

My need to talk to others to help me come to grips was well met by family, friends, and close associates. If they had not been there for me, I believe a support group would have been an imperative.

A UCLA study of sixty-eight patients with melanoma cancer underscores the important connection between mind and body. Of the thirty-four patients who did not get any psychological help, ten had died five to six years later and three others had recurrences. Of the thirty-four who had a six-week program of group support, focusing on the nature of the disease, stress management, and nutrition there were only three deaths and four recurrences. Dr. Fawzy I. Fawzy, who conducted the program, concluded that the group with higher stress produced more natural cortisol, which depressed the immune system's ability to fight their cancer. This led me to a curious inquiry. Did my own frantic existence, which I felt successfully distracted me from my condition, actually cause the suppression of my immune system and a moderation of my symptoms?

I was fortunate years ago to meet Mits Aoki, a minister turned healer from Hawaii. Mits combines western and eastern spirituality in getting you to rid yourself of your emotional and physical baggage in order to help heal yourself. Mits joked about his own background. He said, "I'm like a banana, yellow on the outside and white on the inside." He brought your spirituality, of whatever background, to the surface.

Mits had a healing power. He could move his hands over your body at a distance of about six inches, and you could sense the presence of an electrical field. When his hands hovered over my "guts," there was a sense of heat, which we both felt. He could easily put you into a suspended, calming state. It was very therapeutic and very inspiring to be around him. He spoke so simply, yet at such a lofty philosophical, spiritual level. I truly believe he healed himself of cancer several years ago. There is much that western medicine does not know of eastern healing.

Transcendental Meditation (TM) was popularized in the United States by Maharishi Mahesh Yogi. The simple technique involves the repetition of a secret word, sound, or phrase as a "mantra," in order to prevent distracting thoughts. The technique is used twice daily for twenty minutes. Herbert Benson, M.D., reports that Harvard researchers who studied the Maharishi's technique and found a marked decrease in the body's oxygen consumption and decrease in the body's rate of metabolism. During sleep it takes five hours for oxygen consumption to reduce 8 percent, while TM practitioners can reduce it between 10 and 20 percent in three minutes. TM also reduces heart rate, respiration rate, and blood lactate levels, reversing the symptoms of anxiety and stress.

Communication has proved to be my most powerful weapon against the anger, fear, stress, and loneliness caused by chronic illness. Sharing life's burdens and blessings with family and friends allows them to fall into perspective. Burdens do not seem so great, and blessings seem to abound. I have also found that writing helps me better frame my thoughts. I wrote a novel, *In the Name of the People*, in 1976 and 1977. Even in his weakened state, my stricken law partner was my most enthusiastic audience and my most constructive critic. It was something we shared that transcended his suffering. It was my way of creating a little order out of a seemingly chaotic existence.

Phyllis Rose, writing about George Eliot, a famous nineteenth century female novelist, observed:

> In her bargain with life, the body's humiliation was the soul's enrichment; one prospered at the other's expense.

I believe that if I had been healthy, I would not have

been inspired to write the four books I have literally given birth to. The process challenges you to focus your thoughts, emotions, expectations, fears, and hopes. It has proved to be a wonderful catharsis for me. I hope it has also helped those around me to understand me and what I am dealing with. I know it has for some. Some of my closest friends who read early drafts of this book commented that they had never realized what I was really going through or understood the thoughts and feelings it prompted in me. In the absence of my written exploration of it, they might never have understood. That lack of understanding might have created an unspoken distance between us.

I also credit communication with keeping me positively focused at the most difficult of times. In 1981 and 1982, I wrote *The Money Tree*. Despite my physical travails, I wanted to focus on what a privilege it is to be an American and to have the most unfettered opportunity on earth to pursue one's hopes and dreams. In 1992 and 1993, in the midst of both business and health reversals, I wrote *Fear of Failure*, which focused on using that fear as a motivating force to bring forth our best effort.

I was fortunate to get an interview on CNN about *Fear of Failure*, but it was a near disaster physically. The Los Angeles studio was about a twenty minute drive away, and then some late-breaking news pushed the schedule back. I was not doing well, and hoped I would be able to hold myself together long enough to do the interview before dealing with impending intestinal fireworks. Another brief broadcast delay sent me scrambling to the executive washroom, where I had a nightmarish session dealing with pain spasming and massive elimination. I tried to rush the process and hustled back to the studio. I felt drained and, looking at myself on the monitor, muttered,

"You look like hell!" Everyone in the control room was amused, and Peggy came in to wipe off my forehead and to let me know I was on shortly. I took some deep breaths and moments later the interviewer asked me, "Do you consider yourself a success?"

Here I was before a nationwide audience being asked one of those unanswerable questions, and I was barely functioning. I realized we were "live," with no time for reflection, so I said I was only a success by Winston Churchill's definition: "Success is going from failure to failure without loss of enthusiasm." An adrenaline surge got me through the rest of the interview. It was a relief. Only Peggy and I knew how close I had come to missing it completely.

The human body is remarkable in its ability to make the necessary adjustments to deal with the wear and tear of everyday life, neglect, and abuse, and the onslaught of outside invaders. When it cannot make adjustments on its own, the body mercifully lets you know. It tells you that you cannot function effectively without sleep, you cannot withstand unlimited amounts of stress, you cannot subject yourself to excessive food intake or alcohol or drug consumption. When you experience physical symptoms such as pain or inflammation, it is the body's way of alerting you that you will have to make certain adjustments to preserve your good health. If you simply take medication to mask your physical symptoms, you risk a worsening of the underlying condition and take on the additional risks of side-effects of the medication. For example, aspirin is a wonder drug in reducing pain and inflammation. Aspirin may, however, impede the interaction between platelet release and connective tissue and result in some blood loss. Antibiotics and steroids were miracle breakthroughs, but if overused they can endanger the body more than the underlying condition being treated.

If you listen to your body, your mind, and your soul, you will be attuned to the many healing alternatives available to you. By accessing many possibilities, you will have a wide experience from which to choose your best options. Some choices you will discard immediately and some you will give up over time. But, if you allow your body the time to tell you what heals and what harms, you can piece together the combination of medical and alternative treatments, lifestyle, diet, and regimen that is most responsive to your needs and most conducive to healing.

V

DEALING WITH
STRESS AND FEAR

I have given a good deal of thought to the effects of stress on the progression of my condition. Stress has never been a negative word for me because, without stress, steel could not be forged, diamonds could not be formed, and mankind's remarkable achievements would not have been possible. I have always tried to give my best effort under stress.

Though stress has developed a negative connotation, it can result from happy, positive events, such as meeting a wonderful person or winning an athletic contest, as well as from negative experiences. Hans Selye, the noted expert on stress, emphasizes that the human body actually depletes itself of certain critical resources in the course of compensating for abnormal nervous activity. We experience a good deal of stress from the act of anticipation. A normal child undergoes stress awaiting Christmas morning and the opening of presents almost as much as he suffers in dreading an upcoming visit to the dentist. The gambler (who comes to believe he is immune from gambling stress) actually lives in a world of anticipation— clearly, his world is more anticipation than realization. And so it is with many who reach beyond their normal grasp for attainment of unrealistic goals. The level of stress may depend, then, on the level of realism of your expectations.

I associate only positive stress with my first eleven years of experience in the entrepreneurial world. Perhaps my partners and I were so preoccupied with an almost continuing stream of difficulties that risk and stress became an accepted part of our environment. However, it is a rare businessman who escapes unscathed from the ravages of stress. Even if he has a strong constitution, he must consider both his emotional and physical capacities for stress, a virtual bedfellow of risk. Much is made, for example, of the pressure to win in sports and politics, because the struggle occurs in the public eye. But compare that to the pressure on the businessman who is faced with almost certain failure, desperately negotiating on the phone with creditors, suppliers, and customers, and maybe even a carnivorous opportunist seeking to gain control of the enterprise. At such a time, his total resources, health, career, and sense of self-worth may be on the line. I would find this out first-hand.

The truly healthy businessman is one who is able to make a decision when it is required and move on. The decision is made, the event is concluded. As has been pointed out by Dr. Meyer Friedman and Dr. Ray H. Rosenman in *Type A Behavior and Your Heart*, the most significant trait of the Type A man is that he "incessantly strives to accomplish too much." Time works against him. Those who succeed emotionally and physically at the game of ambition have one thing in common—the ability to work from an agenda rather than a schedule. Decisions have varying degrees of importance, but each must, if possible, be decided as if it has a life cycle of its own. Only when all the relevant factors are known can a rational and effective decision be made. And, except in unusual cases where time is a critical and uncontrollable factor, good management will allot ample time for making effective decisions. If the "hurry sickness" enters in, it almost invariably results from an apprehension on the part of the decision maker that events will intervene to frustrate the decision he presently views as optimum.

Sadly, it was probably extraordinary time pressure on Alvin Feldman that precipitated his death at his own hand; he was apparently a victim of executive stress. Feldman was the former president of Continental Airlines who attempted to orchestrate an employee purchase of the company rather than submit to an outside takeover. Roger S. Veninga, of the University of Minnesota School of Public Health, describes the executive stress syndrome as first being evidenced by "a pattern of sleep disturbances in which an executive goes night after night—either unable to sleep or waking constantly—with office problems on his mind. That quickly leads to a lack of enthusiasm, self-doubt and an inability to make decisions. And finally, in the most serious stage, the executive feels a deep sense of isolation, insisting that no one else can possibly understand what he is going through."

Those who are simply not capable of feeling under

control in the frenzied world of business should be apprised of the possible ravages of stress. *Type A Behavior and Your Heart*, focusing on the health problems of those with an aggressive spirit, points out that the body "does not distinguish between a man struggling against time and one struggling against another man, and makes the organs . . . discharge the same kind of chemicals. . . ." Thus, the typical entrepreneur may be faced with the same health risks, particularly involving the heart, as a man with free-floating hostilities.

Most entrepreneurs and executives are loath to take professional advice to slow down. It seems endemic to the breed to believe that it is better to go out like a flash doing something you love than live a routine existence. In short, you won't catch those Type A sorts dying of boredom! But should you make a fortune and lose your health, you might find you would readily give up what you had gained for what you had lost. If you are not one of those rare adventurers who are totally at peace with risk, you should consider ways of reducing stress.

Many companies are turning to "wellness" programs, primarily for top executives. These programs look at an individual's total being, not just physical fitness. Donald Ardell, who is co-author of the book *Planning for Wellness*, says the programs aim at behavior modifications, stressing the importance of feeling good. "I like to tell people wellness is for fun, romantic, hip, sexy and free. People who practice it are stronger, better looking, have higher morale and more antibodies against disease." Clearly, outlets for stress produce a healthier, more effective decision maker.

I know now that "wellness" requires keeping stress in balance, but for eleven years I had gradually increased my stress level by taking on greater and greater risks.

Whether due to stubbornness, tunnel vision, arrogance, or inexperience, I by nature believed that all problems were solvable somehow, and eleven years of experience had done nothing to change my attitude.

But on July 30, 1990, my faith in the American Dream and in the belief that perseverance and dedication would inevitably prevail, as if by some natural law, was put to the most severe test. Only days before, our family had joyfully celebrated our daughter's wedding to her childhood sweetheart. We had opened our home to a host of friends and relatives and shared with them our happiness with our family and our life. The rewards of the previous eleven years of entrepreneurial frenzy seemed assured and I thought deserved. We had been successfully involved in the acquisition and turnaround of such companies as Standard Felt, Bell Helmets, Riddell Sporting Goods, and Van de Kamp's Bakers. We were also part of the redevelopment and partial restoration of the landmark Huntington Hotel in Pasadena, California, and its future success seemed clear.

Then, a phone call alerted me that Van de Kamp's Bakers, much beloved in Southern California for seventy-five years, would be placed in bankruptcy by the owner to whom we had sold out three years earlier. We still had some outstanding guarantees to the company's landlord, mortgage lender, and pension plan. If Van de Kamp's could not meet its obligations, we could be exposed to substantial financial loss.

In 1987, we had made a strategic error in judgment. We counted on the Van de Kamp's buyer's word that he would replace us personally as guarantors of the company's multimillion dollar obligations under its lease, property, mortgage, and pension plan. Our buyer had represented to us a net worth that was more than enough to secure our release from these obligations. But, despite our efforts to get him to perform, he never carried out his promise, leaving us exposed to obligations that a healthy Van de Kamp's would have had no problem absorbing. A defunct Van de Kamp's and our apparently insolvent buyer potentially left those millions of dollars in obligations to us.

Three days later on August 2, 1990, Saddam Hussein invaded Kuwait and the future of the travel and hotel industries was immediately under a dark cloud. No one was travelling anywhere. Everyone was at home glued to CNN for the next several months. As it turned out, we reopened the hotel as the Ritz-Carlton, Huntington Hotel in the immediate aftermath of Desert Storm. In short, almost overnight, we faced a financial crisis.

Years ago, I heard a talk by Larry Wilson, a lecturer on personal motivation, who compared life to the fiddler on the roof. The fiddler's true fulfillment is in making beautiful music. His only problem is to avoid falling off the roof. If 95 percent of his energy is devoted to clinging to the eaves, it is doubtful he will play much music with the remaining 5 percent. But if he can just learn to steady himself, have confidence in his balance, and perhaps even look out and survey the beauty of the world around him, he is likely to make beautiful music indeed. If we do fall off the roof of life, it is now most likely caused by the fear of falling. Suddenly, I was challenging myself not to fear falling from the roof and instead to devote all my creative energies to making beautiful music. This turns out to be more easily said than done when you are hanging on to the roof with both hands!

My partners and I closed ranks and put together contingency plans. Our personal banker hung in there with us at a time an understanding bank was hard to find. My family members willingly went on an austerity budget. My friends urged me on but would still be my friends even if our best-laid plans should prove unsuccessful. One said, "You won't have failed because the sun will still come up the next morning, you will still be your resourceful self, and you'll get back to doing what you do well." If that was the worst that could happen, I realized I could live with it and never looked back. Instead, I approached our seemingly gargantuan problems with new vigor and enthusiasm.

I awakened one morning with a real sense of the adventure I had experienced the previous twelve years and all that it had meant to me, to my partners, and to our families. The defeats and the losses we had suffered were just transitory and in no way negated the value and the fulfillment of our journey together, nor our future together. With what we had learned from our adversity, we would find the wisdom and strength to carry on no matter what the eventual outcome.

Had I experienced a high level of stress during these difficult times? Of course I had. Had it worsened my medical symptoms? Probably, at times. Would I trade those trying years for a risk-free existence? Never.

Stress may cause or exacerbate health problems, but life without stress is life without meaning. You must find the balance of risks and rewards in your own life that are in sync with your emotional and physical make-up. You can also pursue your dreams with more confidence and enthusiasm if you remember that failures are an essential ingredient in the life formula of any successful person, in any field of pursuit. Never to have failed is never to have tested your limits. Rather than having the "fear of failure" hold you back, you can instead use it as an empowering force to bring out your best.

Only if you allow your chronic illness to serve as an excuse not to try will you have failed. Any effort you make to overcome your physical limitations will produce its own rewards.

VI

THE BOOK OF JOB

In 1993, when my Crohn's symptoms were particularly severe and my two troubled business investments looked most bleak, my mother sent me a copy of *The Book of Job* (translated and with an introduction by Stephen Mitchell). It was intended as a light-hearted reminder that we all have our troubles, and we chuckled about it together. But it was to take on far greater meaning for me.

I had not read *The Book of Job* since I immersed myself in the study of the Old and New Testaments as a college freshman. I was reminded of the paradox that Job is a Gentile, trying to come to some comprehension of God. His age-old theme, that he is an unjust victim, was later

embraced by the Jews and made a part of the Old Testament. In Western culture, the patience of Job is prover-
bial, but the Job of the Old Testament is, in fact, the
antithesis of patience. He is angry at God for punishing
him and his family for no reason. He concludes that,
because suffering comes from God, God is unjust. Stephen
Mitchell observes that the summation of Job's anxiety and
anger is "Why me?" and that there is no answer because
it is the wrong question.

As a lifelong Presbyterian, a sect inspired by the severe
John Calvin, I never felt life should be easy. My father
often reminded me that I should be making "constructive
use of my time," a refrain I passed on to my children on
numerous occasions. Unlike Job, I did not expect there
was any particular reward for "good works," but that the
doing of good was its own reward. However, after fifteen
years of physical suffering and three of financial reversals,
I was ready to exclaim "enough is enough!" I empathized
with Job's lament more than at any other time in life. I
started questioning "Why me?"

Mitchell observes that "God will not hear Job, but Job
will see God." This struck me as very profound because
we cannot know God's grand design, but we can see the
wonder of life and appreciate its awesomeness. Job and
his friends agree that there are limits to human understanding, but they have no sense of just how limited.
Mitchell says Job has to let go of his primitive notions of
God before he can appreciate God as the source of primal
energy, indestructible power, and absolute joy.

Once we see ourselves as a part of God's plan rather
than victims of circumstances, we are freed to behold the
beauty and magnificence of creation. Once we can utilize
the visible metaphors around us to "see" God, life takes

on a more elevated meaning. The lion and the antelope are part of a delicate life balance. The lion hunts down the injured and the sick of the herd. The antelope who are caught and sustain the pride are not victims. They are part of the cycle of life. In those terms, Job begins to understand the folly of trying to project his own moral sense on the universe. He says, "I have spoken of the unspeakable and tried to grasp the infinite."

Reading and contemplating *The Book of Job* was wonderfully comforting to me at a time I was caught up with the frustrating details of my life. Rather than focus on the offending circumstances, it allowed me to transcend my troubles and find joy in the life I have been blessed with. I realized that I no longer needed to see my life in Calvinist terms, involving the "shoulds," the "ought-to's," and the "musts." I could give myself permission to set aside time for spiritual reflection and renewal, and thereby elevate my vision of life's purpose beyond transient accomplishments.

While that vision did not immediately heal my body, it greatly nourished my soul. The epilogue to the ancient story of Job finds him blessed by God. Job had an abundance of worldly possessions, a large and healthy family, and lived to see his great-grandchildren. The epilogue was evidently written by popular demand to provide a happy ending. But, to me, it trivializes the importance of Job's enlightenment after prolonged suffering, for his ultimate reward was not material possessions but an enlightened spirituality.

The mind, like its Creator, surpasses human understanding. I am convinced that the brain can help heal the body, but only if we can reach a state of enlightenment that reduces the myriad of conflicting signals it receives, particularly from a body stressed by day-to-day frustrations. Once the mind and the spirit are focused, healing can proceed. I do not expect miraculously to attain that state of being, but I have commenced the process. As we were taught early in our lives, "God helps those who help themselves."

VII

LIVING WITH
CHRONIC ILLNESS

There is a camaraderie that can develop among chronically-ill patients. All of us have felt distanced from well-meaning people who cannot possibly know what we have been through. We have felt de-humanized by hospital personnel who meant no offense in treating us as numbers rather than people—they were just doing their job. We have feared never being whole again, never being able to enjoy a normal existence. We have worried about being or becoming a burden to others and about not being able to meet our responsibilities. We wonder why we got sick and whether we bore some responsibility for our condition. We all shut off much of the world from these feelings, opting to tell everyone "I'm fine, really."

I know so many people who have dealt with so much with grace and courage. They have my admiration and my caring. Two good friends stand out. One had polio as a child. Most people age fifty or over have seen the devastating damage childhood polio can cause. My friend now deals with the cruel symptoms of post-polio syndrome as an adult, which has only recently been identified in adult patients who suffered acute poliomyelitis in their youth. Her condition has never held her back. A mother of four, she has led an active life. She was a Girl Scout leader and pitched her own tent, despite the hindrance of crutches. One fall Saturday afternoon she went to a USC game with her husband at the Los Angeles Coliseum, a facility not designed for easy access to those with physical disabilities. In fact, going down forty or fifty narrow steps to USC's booster seats is a peril to the fully able-bodied. It began to rain at halftime. Her husband asked if she would like to leave early and she said, "Absolutely not."

"Why not?" he wondered.

"Because I want full credit!" she responded, smiling.

Another friend suffers from polycystic disease of the kidney, an insidious and hereditary disease, which can also attack the liver. The patient develops numerous cysts in the kidney, back pain, and infections caused by reduced kidney function. The disease can be fatal due to kidney failure. This can be avoided by dialysis or kidney transplants.

My friend did not want to become permanently dependent on a dialysis machine, so she took her treatment into her own hands. She flew to several well-regarded medical centers around the country to have her tissue typed and all arrangements made for a kidney transplant on short notice. It would be difficult to find a relative who could be a donor because of the prevalence of the disease within families. Eventually, she received a call from Dallas that a suitable transplant had been identified due to the tragic death of a young boy. She flew there and had the transplant performed. She often thinks of the young boy whose own life was sadly cut short but who gave her life.

My friend rarely dwelled on the depression caused by her condition. When she felt unable to cope, she would pull herself together and go to the childhood oncology department at UCLA and volunteer her time, brightening the day of young cancer patients. She said, "I always leave there recognizing what a wonderful life I've had and how lucky I am to be alive." She somehow manages to lead a very full life. That is, of course, when her friends see her. When we don't, it is because she is dealing with tough times on her own terms at home.

My friend and I spoke a few years ago with another chronically ill patient about the heartache of steroids. I asked them both, "Do you get a normal night's sleep?" It turned out none of us slept more than three or four hours a night on steroids. My friend asked, "How's the weight?" and we all laughed, because we had all gained immense amounts of weight.

There is a wonderful sense of relief in sharing with others who understand your plight. It is nice to know you are not alone in your suffering or your misery. It somehow makes it easier to fight on.

Sometimes you do not really know someone well but feel a *sympatico*. I saw a doctor at a cocktail party, who I had not known well until he married one of our friends. He had an advanced case of lymphoma, and was enduring frequent transfusions because of his inability to produce platelets. His existence, by some standards, was a nightmare. He came up to me and asked me how I was holding up. I was taken aback. He was battling for his very life, yet he was expressing concern about me.

I started calling him once a week to see how he was doing. When he was up to it, we had long talks. He knew he had very little time to live, yet he seemed to expend all his energy for others. He was particularly troubled about his daughter who was having difficulty getting into medical school. She was on the waiting list of a good school but was told she was well down the list. Unfortunately, they normally had only one or two drop out of an entering class for personal or health reasons.

I asked him, "Which school?"

He said, "St. Louis University, the same school my dad and I went to. It would mean a lot to me if she got in this year." What he did not say was that he was certain he would not be around next year.

I recalled that Peggy's uncle had gone to St. Louis Medical School and had a long-time friendship with the Chancellor Emeritus. I asked my friend if he would like me to have a letter written on behalf of his daughter. He explained that a few influential people had already tried unsuccessfully, but it would mean a lot if I would try.

A letter recommending this outstanding young woman was written to the former Chancellor, but a polite letter was sent back by return mail explaining there was nothing they could do.

It seemed fair for me to press the point. I put in a call to the office of the Chancellor Emeritus and spoke to his assistant, explaining the situation. I said, "I'm sure you have a lot of qualified applicants on your waiting list but not many whose father and grandfather were alums. And, I doubt if you have any whose father's dying wish is for his daughter to follow in his footsteps."

"It's really that serious?" she asked.

"I don't want to be dramatic," I responded, "but he isn't expected to live more than a few months."

The next day, this wonderful woman called me back and told me, "I'm not going to explain the details, but your friend's daughter will be admitted on a probationary basis."

I called my friend and he was overcome with happiness for his daughter. He said, "I want you to know that, even if she hadn't gotten in, this is one of the kindest things anyone has ever done. You are a wonderful friend."

I have the feeling he had many wonderful friends because he transcended his devastating illness and made you feel he truly cared about you. Sadly, he died a few months later, but the way he lived his few years under constant threat of death was an example for everyone whose life he touched.

The impediments of chronic illness should in no way be minimized by the recitation of many people's successful experiences in living with it. Everyone who has been confronted with its inherent limits has undoubtedly experienced heartaches, disappointments, setbacks, depression, embarrassment, and self-pity. It is only human to wish to be able-bodied and healthy. But it is inspiring for all of us to know that our conditions not only can be overcome, they can make us stronger and help us lead more meaningful lives.

Chronic illness can make it nearly impossible to perform a "normal" job, involving full-time employment away from home. When you have at best two or three good hours a day, the logistics of commuting to the office and going to meetings can consume your reservoir of strength. Fortunately, this is a whole new world in which you can be productive from anywhere with access to a fax machine and a phone. For the five years following our

Ritz-Carlton and Van de Kamp's reversals, I dedicated my efforts toward solving or at least mitigating those problems. During that time, I juggled a busy schedule between my nearby office and home.

As my partners and I wound down our crushing load of liabilities and challenges, it became clear that I had nearly exhausted my hard-earned investment capital. I would either have to repeat my foray into business turnarounds in an environment far more difficult than had greeted us in 1979, or I would have to find a normal job. I had not actively practiced law for fifteen years. I had not had a boss since 1968 when I worked in the corporate finance department of a large Los Angeles law firm. When you have been out of circulation for that long, you cannot simply pick up where you left off, even though I had been in constant touch with my law firm in my "of counsel" role. But my old clients have been well-served by my former law partners—that means fourteen-hour-a-day accessibility to serve those clients' needs. I was less physically able to do that now than when I left in 1979.

I could not keep normal hours. I would not qualify for health or disability insurance coverage. I would not immediately be able to bring in additional clients. In short, I would not be bringing anything new to my law firm relationship.

Many of the same considerations probably would also apply in the field of corporate finance. This field includes investment bankers, merchant bankers, conventional banks, other institutional lenders, merger and acquisition brokers, capital equipment leasing brokers, and the like, all of whom I have worked with over the years. But, this is a fast-moving, intense, competitive arena, where nothing, including health, gets in the way of performance. A "head hunter" would not identify me as a priority prospect in this field, notwithstanding almost three decades of experience.

Another factor I was unexpectedly confronted with was my age of over fifty. Friends warned me that I would hear code words from prospective employers, such as "overqualified," or that they could not "afford" me. Of course, an employer would prefer to make an investment in a bright, aspiring thirty-year-old, with a potentially long career with the company (even though that bias may be against the law). A young, healthy person can travel anywhere, anytime, move to another city, work long hours, and would not have a level of experience that might prove threatening to an immediate superior. Let's face it, no one wants to hire someone who might compete for his or her job.

After considerable reflection, I was horrified to conclude that I was probably unemployable for a normal job. Instead, I resolved that I would commence a corporate finance consulting firm, keeping together my lean and mean, loyal, and extremely competent office staff, and attempt to let the marketplace know that I was available.

There is an expression that "things are sold, not bought," so availability does not equate to hireability. While I had consulted for numerous friends and acquaintances over the years, without charge, I simply was not perceived in the marketplace as someone for hire. For those who knew of my availability, many assumed I could not solve their problems within my perceived narrow window of functioning each day. I certainly cannot fault anyone for that impression. Others evidently thought their needs were not of the dimension of the highly visible companies and problems I had worked on for sixteen years.

While I resolved to continue my consulting arm, I also concluded that I must embark on something I could control myself, no matter how difficult. This meant seeking another turnaround acquisition, a field in which I was very comfortable despite its violent swings of fortune. I found, in reestablishing my contacts in the world of corporate finance, that the many people with whom I had dealings over the course of sixteen years were anxious to do business again. It had not been easy to identify prospective acquisitions in the late 1970's and 1980's, or to solve the myriad of business problems my partners and I took on, and the 1990's will prove no different. Of course, the entrepreneurial world will always be fraught with risk. But, most importantly, chronic illness will not prevent me from again pursuing its opportunities.

VIII

THE HISTORY OF CROHN'S DISEASE

While few significant breakthroughs have occurred to improve the treatment of Crohn's disease, or to hasten its cure, it has helped me a great deal to understand the disease and to put it in personal and historical perspective. The more you understand your condition, the easier it is to accept its limitations and get on with your life.

Crohn's disease has an interesting history. There were fifty-six cases in nineteenth-century medical literature that documented symptoms very similar to what is now known as Crohn's disease.

In 1859 in London, a young woman was thought to be suffering from arsenic poisoning. Her husband, who was having a torrid and quite public affair at the time, which was shocking in Victorian society, was suspected of trying to do away with her. The woman, whose condition proved fatal, is now thought to have been the first documented case of Crohn's disease. Her autopsy showed scattered ulcerations throughout the colon. Sadly for the woman's husband, the real cause of her death was not understood at the time of his trial for her murder by poisoning. He was convicted and hanged.

In 1913, a Scottish physician carefully documented the findings in thirteen patients who clearly had the condition later reported by Dr. Crohn. The common denominators were spasming, diarrhea, intestinal obstruction, and inflamed intestines.

Dr. Burrill Crohn had a patient in 1930 with similar symptoms whose sister required surgery for the condition several years later. It may be the first reported incidence of familial predilection to the disease. Dr. Crohn's study of twelve patients with the disease was presented to the American Medical Association in 1932.

The inflammatory bowel diseases ulcerative colitis and Crohn's disease afflict hundreds of thousands of Americans. Some estimates, in fact, run as high as two million. The number of cases appear to be divided evenly between the two conditions. For centuries, these afflictions were thought to be an intestinal tuberculosis. In the 1950's, ulcerative colitis was distinguished from Crohn's disease, despite their overlapping symptoms. For years, treatment of these conditions has involved a balancing of Azulfidine, a sulfa drug that became available in the 1930's, corticosteroids, such as prednisone, which were first available in the 1950's, and surgery. While much more is now known, and other medication is in use, that balancing act remains much the same today. High hopes by researchers for drugs such as interferon, cyclosporin, BCG (tuberculosis) vaccine, turned to disappointment.

Crohn's disease can be confined to the colon, the ileum (between the large and small intestine), the duodenum (in the small intestine, near the stomach) or the esophagus, or to more than one of those locations.

Crohn's disease seems to be heavily concentrated in industrialized nations such as the Scandinavian countries, England, Scotland, Israel, and the United States.

President Dwight D. Eisenhower had Crohn's disease but had only four acute attacks over the course of his lifetime, the first at age nineteen and the last while he was in the White House. He had emergency surgery to relieve an intestinal obstruction in June 1956, and the news made national headlines. Apparently, he suffered sharp intestinal pain for more than thirty years before doctors diagnosed his illness. Five months after surgery, he was re-elected President.

In the mid-1970's, researchers at fourteen U.S. hospitals formed the National Cooperative Crohn's Disease Study. The group set out to assess the normal course of the disease and to evaluate various forms of treatment. They developed a standardized grading system to enable physicians to determine the severity of an individual patient's condition. They concluded that Azulfidine and prednisone were effective in treating attacks but not in preventing flare-ups over the long term.

In 1981, English scientists reported they had isolated a mycobacteria-like organism in the abdominal lymph nodes of half of Crohn's and ulcerative colitis patients they studied. In 1984, an American group isolated a different mycobacteria in two out of eleven patients. Goats who were fed the mycobacterium developed Crohn's-like symptoms, but these results have not yet satisfied re-searchers that a direct cause-effect relationship exists.

Researchers had identified chromosome six as the home of at least two genetic markers, one for Crohn's and one for ulcerative colitis.

It is time for Crohn's disease to overcome the stereo-types that even its sufferers have shared. To accept Meyer Blinder's son's characterization of the disease as "too hu-miliating, too dirty, too scary," and too close to everyone's personal experience, victimizes those hundreds of thou-sands afflicted with the condition in the U.S. Greater awareness of the condition by those who suffer its ill effects, and their family and friends, is the first step in overcoming its chronic symptoms. Increasing awareness among physicians about how to diagnose and treat it is an important next step in limiting suffering from the condi-tion. Lastly, public and governmental education about Crohn's disease, and many other "orphan" diseases that afflict millions of Americans, may prevent their de-emphasis by our health care system and increase the prospects for improved treatment and an eventual cure. The same level of care should be available for those few million patients as it is to those with more common diseases.

IX

THE IMPACT OF HEALTH CARE REFORM

It will become far more difficult to overcome chronic illness in this country if we emasculate the extraordinary strengths of the U.S. health care system. There has been a political drumbeat out of Washington about a health-care crisis in America. President Clinton told a nationwide audience in February 1993 that "a lot of Americans don't have health care." While some Americans do not have health care *insurance*, it is incorrect to assume Americans do not have access to health care. Doctors and hospitals across the country provide health care to many, especially young people, who choose not to purchase health insurance due to its cost (and because they feel they are healthy), to those between jobs who may not currently

have coverage (more than 10 percent of the uninsured actually have annual incomes exceeding $50,000 per year),
and to the poor (only about 30 percent of the uninsured)
who cannot afford insurance. But federal law requires that
hospital emergency rooms screen everyone, and if treatment is needed, it must be provided. Emergency room
doctors have a professional organization, which has the
following motto: "Our specialty is devoted to treating
everyone in need, no questions asked." In short, *no one*
in America is denied critical health care.

Assuredly, there is a better, and less costly, way to provide health care to the less than 20 percent of our population which is uninsured at any one time, but it is not
grounds for socializing the best health care system in the
world. To turn the system over to the federal bureaucracy
is certain to increase costs and decrease benefits. As one
observer put it "Americans feel they will get a system with
the compassion of the IRS, the dispatch of the Post Office,
and cost structure of the Defense Department!"

Medicare, enacted in 1965, has failed to provide quality care at less cost to forty million private-sector patients
aged sixty-five and over. Why should we believe the federal government can do a better job for younger people?
Vice President Al Gore, in addressing the problems of the
federal bureaucracy, stated that it "wastes 48 cents of every tax dollar." How does this square with Mrs. Clinton's
dream of collectivizing the delivery of more care, at less
cost, with no decline in quality?

Senator Patrick Moynihan, former Chairman of the
powerful Senate Finance Committee, publicly rebuked the
President about his priorities: "We don't have a health-
care crisis in this country. We do have a welfare crisis."
Moynihan insisted that welfare reform be given priority,
and succeeded, in 1994, in eliciting a proposal from the

White House to revolutionize welfare. When former Senate Majority Leader George Mitchell tried to force Moynihan to step aside and let the health care plan through, Moynihan is alleged to have threatened to expose the plan as a huge tax increase in disguise. The Los Angeles *Times* magazine stated that Moynihan has ensured that, at every opportunity, his "committee took note of the fact that American medicine has a record of breathtaking achievements." He continually reminds would-be health care reformers of the Hippocratic Oath: "First do no harm."

As the Clinton Administration continues to press for health care centralization, we should step back and assess what we have, and what we are likely to lose. I sincerely fear President Clinton's proposal for emphasizing generalists to lower the cost of overall medical care. In a world where I did not have ready access to the medical specialists who have kept me going, I could be totally disabled or dead. There are dozens of "orphan" diseases, such as Crohn's disease, with inadequate research budgets, frequent misdiagnoses, and mistreatment. In the aggregate, there are millions of Americans afflicted who should be entitled to access to specialized care, particularly if they are willing and able to pay for it.

Fred Barnes in *The New Republic* magazine points out that the best measure of a national health care system is how it treats the seriously ill, because infant mortality rates and life expectancy (frequently-used yardsticks) are affected by factors unrelated to health care (such as drug use, homicides, and other evidences of social problems). Barnes reports that the death rate for an enlarged prostate in the U.S. is one-seventh the rate in Sweden, one-fourth of Great Britain's rate, and one-third of Germany's. The death rate from an ulcer of the stomach or intestine is by far the lowest in the U.S., as is the death rate from a hernia or intestinal obstruction. This list also includes stomach cancer, cervical cancer, and uterine cancer. The U.S. is second in death rates from breast cancer and heart attack. Overall, the U.S. has the best survival rate in the world for serious illness.

The availability of medical technology to patients in the U.S. is far ahead of the rest of the world. This machinery and equipment is particularly needed for acute care. Exciting new medical breakthroughs and a quickening pace of technological advances promise to revolutionize the delivery of health care in America in the twenty-first century. Only the free market (albeit modified by government regulation) will be able to assure that the right allocation of talent and resources is available to meet these rapid changes. Government has proved, time and time again, its incapacity to second-guess or supersede the marketplace.

In their quest for market versus managed economies, Eastern European nations were influenced by Friedrich Hayek's book *Road to Serfdom*, which states: ''The substitution of central planning for competition would require central direction of a much greater part of our lives than ever before.'' It is ironic that, as the rest of the world is embracing the free market, the Clinton Administration is seeking to steer the U.S. toward central planning.

I served on a California hospital board in the 1980's and observed the dramatic changes in the way hospitals operated. In the early part of the decade, they were cost-plus operations, simply passing on their costs plus a return on investment to their patients. But the establishment of ''managed care'' by the State of California in 1982 changed the entire environment. Hospitals were suddenly forced to compete on the basis of quality and cost. Hospitals had to respond by managing their costs, their staffing, and their procedures in order to compete. From 1983 to 1985, total real hospital costs per capita fell in Califorina, while nationwide costs continued to increase 3 percent above the rate of inflation. Although costs resumed an upturn for the balance of the decade, California's hospital costs still increased only 9 percent in the 1980's, as compared with 30 percent nationally. In the 1990's, California's costs resumed their downtrend. In short, competition works.

The imperfections of the U.S. health care system must, of course, be addressed. Managed care programs must cover a very high percentage of Americans and alternative ways must be found to make coverage reasonably available to all others who can afford it. Only for the small remaining percentage of uninsured should the government play a role.

Widespread popular support for "health reform" claimed by supporters quickly disperses when poll takers get down to specifics. The fact is that a vast majority of Americans like the coverage they have and the flexible health care it provides. Of course, they would like it to be "better, cheaper, faster." Who wouldn't? But most Americans doubt that a new federal bureaucracy can improve quality, reduce cost, or expedite the delivery of treatment. The one objective most agree on is that somehow, some way, some time, everyone should be covered. What they fear is that code words such as "universal coverage" mean that the middle class will end up paying for the poor and the uninsured. The term "single payer" really means that the government is going to preempt our private system of health care and, if we do not like it, there will be no going back.

The proliferation of health management organizations HMOs is already profoundly impacting health care in America. It has brought discipline and competition to the system, but the pervasiveness of the federal bureaucracy is still the driving force behind the health industry. The myriad of federal, state, and HMO rules and regulations make it increasingly difficult to provide quality care to any patient with out-of-the-ordinary needs. Cost control is, of course, an imperative in an industry whose costs were out of control for a generation, but quality is being compromised. My HMO now covers the cost of an annual physical examination but only if I use their approved list of physicians. Their physicians may well be competent, but they do not know what to look for in doing a thorough, responsible physical exam if they do not know the patient. As HMO subscribers are forced by cost considerations to comply with HMO requirements, the general availability of optimal care will inevitably decline in the absence of some flexibility in the system.

HMOs may not provide the perfect solution for the chronically ill, unless such patients are afforded free market access to the best specialists available. Economics may require that the patient absorb a significant portion of the cost.

I have been fortunate to have continuous medical coverage throughout my ordeal, although it has been costly. My office experiences the usual bureaucracy in administering claims, and there have been numerous rate increases as my claims history continues to make our small group an unattractive risk. When our insurance carrier seemed to price our coverage out of affordable range, we explored alternative coverage, but other carriers wanted no part of my volumes of medical history. My disability carrier also wanted no part of me. At the first sign of Crohn's symptoms, back in 1979, they offered me a discounted payoff of my lifetime policy. Life insurance, oddly, was different. I still take a great physical and am insurable without surcharge. Insurers do not care about the quality of my life, only that I stay alive!

The highly-politicized subject of health care reform is an important subject to all Americans, but none more so than the chronically ill and especially the millions with less-common afflictions. There is no more important freedom in a free society than the right to choose your own doctor at a time your health is seriously in danger. It is my fervent hope that this will not prove to be the latest individual freedom that is sacrificed in the name of governmental efficiency or convenience. The results of the 1994 elections would seem to assure that alternatives to socialized medicine will be fully explored.

X

OVERCOMING CHRONIC ILLNESS

I have endured the miseries and indignities of Crohn's disease for over sixteen years. While my worst ongoing symptom of esophageal ulcerations has been significantly reduced, the inflammation, pain, and congestion in the throat have progressed and my intestinal and arthritic symptoms continue unabated. The myriad of other symptoms have not gone away. While I better understand why my parent's friend shot himself rather than deal any longer with this insidious disease, I hope that patients with Crohn's and other chronic illnesses, even in their most acute stages, will instead consider taking responsibility for their own care. Only when you allow a disease or permanent disability to make you its victim does the quality of

91

life become so minimal that ending it is an option. But there is a multitude of options. You can "access the physician within" and elevate the quality and effectiveness of communication with the doctor of your choosing. To make that choice effective, you have to help the doctor know you as intimately as a good friend. Otherwise, you will continually worry whether your doctor has any idea what you are going through. Norman Cousins, who knew Dr. Schweitzer, says that Schweitzer had a serious illness in early middle-age and resolved to remember what he went through in his future dealings with patients. Only by being a patient did Schweitzer realize that a patient's psychology was as important as his diagnosis.

So much depends on the patient. You can access the strength of your friendships and let those close to you be there for you. You can access alternative medicine and therapy to find what best enables you to accept the limitations of your condition and to embrace the meaningful life that still awaits you. You can experiment with diet and exercise to ensure that your physical strength is at an optimal level, enabling you to withstand the worst your condition presents you and to aspire to broader horizons when it relents. You can plan your professional and personal existence around your physical limitations, while continuing to explore and challenge those limits. You can find inspiration in the struggles and triumphs of others and seek to inspire others whose burdens sometimes seem too heavy.

In *Fear of Failure*, I philosophized about what we can learn from dealing with overwhelming difficulties:

> We can learn, or at least strive to learn, not to take ourselves so seriously, to keep our sense of humor, to appreciate our family and friends, to better understand true friendship, to

recognize the good fortune as well as the reversals that come our way, to appreciate the process of striving as much as any success, to better accept shortcomings in others and better recognize our own, to be as generous to others as we can with our time and our resources, to let others help us grow, to marvel at the beauty of the world around us, to understand the rejuvenating power of leisure, to prioritize health over wealth, and most importantly, to appreciate how fragile and special life is.

Limitations can be produced physically, psychologically, by act of God, or accident of birth. The quality of life depends on how you deal with those limits. There is a fine line between resigning yourself to being a victim and accepting certain limitations in the context of continually challenging them. One approach is hopeless, while the other is hopeful.

Dr. Victor E. Frankl, a survivor of Nazi prison camps, wrote in his book *Man's Search for Meaning*: "Everything can be taken from a man but one thing: the last of human freedoms—to choose one's attitude in any given set of circumstances." Accordingly, you are free to overcome your chronic illness and it is a matter of choice. You can choose to set goals for yourself physically, professionally, socially, and personally. You can choose to excel at whatever outlet allows you to transcend your physical limitations. You can maintain a sense of your humor, even if it sometimes approaches "gallows" humor. You can choose to celebrate the joy of life and all of its possibilities, and you can seek an inner sense of peace.

Victor E. Frankl inspires us to choose "optimism in the face of tragedy and in view of the human potential which at its best always allows for: (1) turning human suffering into a human achievement and accomplishment; (2) drawing from guilt the opportunity to change oneself for the better; and (3) drawing from life's transitories an incentive to take responsible action."

This is not to say that any of this will be easy, but to paraphrase Tim Hansel, author of *You Gotta Keep Dancing*, "Life isn't easy, only simple." If you can focus your physical and emotional energy on what you want to make of your life with all its attendant changes and complications, your goal will become simple. You will have chosen the life of adaptivity and creativity, rather than the role of the victim. In short, if you cannot change your circumstances, you must change the way you respond to them.

Reynolds Price, in his book *A Whole New Life*, captures the disbelief in the able-bodied that a chronically-ill person can carry on. He says:

> By very slow inches, the decision to change my life forced itself upon me; and I moved ahead as if a path was actually there and would stretch on a while.

Price chose life and rejected self-pity for the paraplegia that resulted from cancer of the spine at age fifty-one. More than half of his books have been written since his remarkable recovery from an almost-certain death. Looking back, he can still conclude, "I've yet to watch another life that seems to have brought more pleasure to its owner than mine has to me."

Cousins and Price both had physicians who, in effect, signed their death warrants. They have cautioned physicians not to discount the power of the will to live and to be more concerned about the patient than about being right. Cousins was told in 1964 that he had one chance in five hundred to live with a collagen disease of the connective tissue. Ten years later, he saw one of the specialists who had made the diagnosis and told him he "hoped they would be careful about what they said to others; they might be believed and that could be the beginning of the end."

Price was told he had "six months to paraplegia, six months to quadriplegia, six months to death." When the wife of the diagnosing physician learned he had just celebrated his sixtieth birthday, nine years later, she exclaimed, "But that's miraculous."

The testimony of these celebrated authors should be reflected upon by physicians and patients alike. If the patient is encouraged to access all the healing powers at the disposal of the physican and patient, working together, the patient can choose life and overcome a chronic, even apparently-fatal, illness. Cousins observes that "Most doctors recognize that medicine is just as much an art as it is a science and that the important knowledge in medicine to be learned or taught is the way the human mind and body can summon innnermost resources to meet extraordinary challenges."

It would be a cruel hoax to tell chronically-ill patients that, if they adopt a positive attitude, they will be cured and live happily ever after. Then, if they are not miraculously cured, it is obviously the patient's fault for having a bad attitude. Overcoming chronic illness is not about miracle cures, it is about minimizing the negative effects on a meaningful existence that chronic symptoms can cause. The reconstruction of the life of a chronically-ill patient will not proceed in a straight line. It will involve disappointments, relapses, false hopes, and eventual breakthroughs.

No matter how great your physical limitations, you can eventually emancipate yourself from and rise above chronic illness. If you persevere through the long and difficult process of self-awareness and self-discovery, you will have limitless horizons you can pursue.

People underestimate the productive capacity of the chronically-ill and disabled. When I was in law school, I got to know a fellow student who was a quadriplegic. Because he could barely hunt and peck on the typewriter, the administration gave him lengthy extensions of time to complete his exams. As a result, he was near the top of his class. While he could type only one third as fast as others, he could think as fast, if not faster.

There are compensating factors that increase the productivity of the infirmed. The inability to engage in all of the distractions of the able-bodied actually frees you to focus your attention on your newly-adopted priorities. Tim Hansel, physically disabled by a mountain-climbing accident, says his life since the accident has been "the opportunity to be on the steepest learning curve of my own life," and that "the assets have far outweighed the losses and liabilities." He finally realized that it was not his imposed limitations that held him back following the accident but his perception of them. With the help of his religious faith, Hansel chose the joy of life over self-pity and depression. The strength of his attitude now is obvious in his words:

> Joy has more to do with who we are than what we have, more to do with the healthiness of our attitude than the health of our body.

Joanna Baumer Permut had a comparable experience. In *Embracing the Wolf*, she concludes that her ongoing battle with lupus has transformed her and that she is "better equipped to face difficulties" in her life. She is a "more secure individual, comfortable and at peace inside." Equally as important, she and her husband "have learned together that couples can indeed live happily in the face of chronic disease."

JoAnn LeMaistre, Ph.D., the author of *Beyond Rage*, has multiple sclerosis and is a psychotherapist to chronically-ill patients and their families. Her onset of symptoms began six weeks after giving birth to a premature baby and two weeks before her licensing exam in clinical psychology. While it was to prove too much for her now ex-husband, LeMaistre's personal experience with chronically-ill patients would help her and her patients "to be psychologically well while physically sick." As she puts it: "If you have a chronic disease, you need not be emotionally handicapped if you continually strive to be able-hearted." Despite devastating physical limitations, LeMaistre found a way to conduct her clinical practice, to teach at Stanford Medical Center, to speak often at conferences, to raise a daughter as a single parent, and to write a very valuable book for anyone interested in chronic illness.

Victor E. Frankl cites Jerry Long, a quadriplegic, as an example of "the defiant power of the human spirit." Long learned to use a mouth-stick to type and to attend college courses by special telephone. Long is quoted as saying:

> I view my life as being abundant with meaning and purpose. . . . I know that without the suffering, the growth that I have achieved would have been impossible.

The chronically-ill or disabled do not have a problem with productivity if they transcend their symptoms and find self-worth in alternate outlets. Those with a problem are the ones who are left mired in self-pity and depression, but, of course, there are vast numbers of able-bodied in the same state.

These days I only occasionally lapse into feeling sorry for myself when my symptoms worsen or I become nostalgic over my previous existence, but my productivity has only been enhanced by my increased solitary time, my decreased outside activities, and my intense desire to make the most of my situation. This is my fourth book since the onset of my symptoms. My foray into the entrepreneurial world since 1979 has been intensely involving, productive, meaningful, and sometimes agonizing. I credit its diversity and excitement, to some extent, with giving me little time for self-doubt or depression. Of course, the excessive stress may have been a negative factor at times. But none of us has the luxury to keep stress within rigid limits at all times and still lead a productive life. Also, greater stress by far came from my inability to cope with the early stages of chronic illness. But the principal sources of new understanding needed to minimize that stress were personal, not professional—they were my family and friends.

You cannot help but be inspired, as I have been, by the compelling examples of patient power and its importance in overcoming the limitations and heartache of chronic illness. I hope you will become pro-active whatever your condition, find ways to transcend your limitations, and seek to achieve at your highest capacity. You are not alone out there. The chronically-ill and disabled number in the tens of millions in the U.S. Among them, you can find the inspiration to empower your own triumph over circumstances and, in turn, can inspire others to live more positive, productive lives.

You are limited only by your perception of your limits, and your fear of the consequences of trying to free yourself from them. You will never know your potential for growth until you test those limits. If at first you fail, you risk only some embarrassment and frustration. If you never try, you risk missing the limitless wonder of life's possibilities.

PATIENT POWER:
OVERCOMING CHRONIC ILLNESS

James Marshall Galbraith is the author of **Fear of Failure**, featured on CNN, which exhorts readers to use the fear of failure as an empowering, rather than paralyzing force, and **The Money Tree**, which simplifies how anyone can access the free enterprise system. He is also the author of **In the Name of the People**, a novel of political intrigue.

Patient Power is an inspiring account of Galbraith's personal battle with a chronic, debilitating disease and how one truly can overcome chronic illness and lead a life rich with possibilities. Galbraith focuses especially on self empowerment:

"Those of us who suffer from chronic illness often lose sight of the important role we must play in our own medical care. The historical relationship between patient and physician has been a passive one, with the patient trusting that all is in good hands. We have always put physicians on pedestals, assuming they were somehow God-like in knowing what ails us and what treatment to prescribe. In reality, we soon learn that the only thing more amazing than what doctors know is what they don't. And what they especially don't know is us."

BENCHMARK BOOKS
2600 MISSION STREET
SAN MARINO, CALIFORNIA 91108-1676